Patterns

of Impairment

in Specific

Reading

Disability

in collaboration with

Arthur L. Drew
INDIANA UNIVERSITY

Hallgrim Kløve
UNIVERSITY OF WISCONSIN

James Norton
INDIANA UNIVERSITY

Ralph M. Reitan
INDIANA UNIVERSITY

Patterns
of Impairment
in Specific
Reading
Disability

A NEUROPSYCHOLOGICAL INVESTIGATION

Donald G. Doehring
McGILL UNIVERSITY

INDIANA UNIVERSITY PRESS
BLOOMINGTON · LONDON 1968

Indiana University Science Series Number 23
Indiana University, Bloomington, Indiana

PUBLICATION COMMITTEE
Charles J. Vitaliano, *Chairman*
P. Sears Crowell
Richard C. Starr

The Indiana University Science Series was
founded in 1939 for the publication of monographs and occasional papers by members of
the faculty.

to Ann Fuller

whose skill, perseverance, and attention to detail during the collection, organization, and analysis of data enabled us to put together the pieces of this project.

Preface

The investigation reported herein was intended primarily to be a fact-finding survey. It was felt that a comprehensive assessment of the abilities of children with specific reading disability would be very useful, since the majority of theoretical explanations of reading disability have been based upon incomplete knowledge in this respect. The main theoretical consideration in this study was an explicit recognition of the possibility that the pattern of disability of retarded readers might resemble that of adults with lesions of the left cerebral hemisphere. Rather unexpectedly, the analysis of results revealed a high correlation between reading disability and impaired performance of a small set of visual and verbal tasks which required the sequential processing of related material. Although such a finding could be fortuitous, it did suggest the potential value of a certain class of psychological theory as a frame of reference for further research into specific reading disability. An attempt has been made, therefore, to present the details of a factual survey of the abilities of retarded readers and at the same time to indicate a possible direction for a theoretical explanation of reading disability.

This research was carried out during the writer's tenure in the Department of Neurology and the Institute of Psychiatric Research of the Indiana University Medical Center. The main financial support came from grants to Prof. Drew and Prof. Reitan, and from operating funds of the Institute of Psychiatric Research. The research was planned and executed in close collaboration with Arthur L. Drew, M.D., who is Professor of Neurology, Director of the Pediatric Neurology Clinic, and Associate Director of the Institute of Psychiatric Research of the Indiana University Medical Center; Ralph M. Reitan, Ph.D., who is Professor of Psychology in the Department of Neurology and Director of the Neuropsychology Laboratory of the Indiana University Medical Center; and Hallgrim Kløve, Cand. Psychol., who is now Associate Professor in the Department of Neurology, University of Wisconsin. The statistical analyses were carried out and interpreted in collaboration with James Norton, Ph.D., Associate Professor of Biostatistics in the Institute of Psychiatric Research. The bulk of the psychological testing, preparation of test material, scoring and tabulation of data, and case history interviewing was carried out by one research assistant, Mrs. Elizabeth Ann Fuller, B.A., to whom this volume is gratefully dedicated. The writer also wishes to thank Dr. Hildred Schuell for permission to use a research edition of the Minnesota Test for Differential Diagnosis of Aphasia.

Much gratitude must be expressed to the individuals and institutions through whose auspices the children with reading problems and the normal readers were obtained for testing. The approval of the Indianapolis Board of Education was essential to the initiation of the project. Miss Francis Graney, Director of the Reading Clinics of the Indianapolis Public Schools, devoted a great deal of time to the selection of a sample of retarded readers and made many valuable suggestions during the preliminary planning of the study. Monseigneur James P. Galvin, Superintendent of Indianapolis Parochial Schools, very kindly consented to the testing of children from the Parochial Schools, and these children were selected with the close cooperation of Mrs. Mary Cunningham, Coordinator of Remedial Reading in the Indianapolis Parochial Schools. Several retarded readers were also obtained for testing through the cooperation of Mrs. Gertrude Meyers, Director of the Indianapolis Reading Clinic. A precise matching of retarded readers and normal readers in age and Performance IQ was made possible by the opportunity to obtain a sample of normal readers from an entire school population in Markleville, Indiana. This was accomplished through the cooperation of Mr. Joseph F. Best, Trustee of Adams Township, Madison County, Indiana, Mr. Harold Creason, Principal of Fall Creek Heights School, and Mr. Raymond E. Rittman, Principal of Markleville High School.

The writer is greatly indebted to Dr. Caridad Cruz, Fellow in Pediatric Neurology, who carried out the majority of neurological examinations of retarded readers, and travelled from Indianapolis to Markleville to conduct all of the neurological examinations of normal readers. Thanks are also due to Drs. Peter W. Morgan and Harold Booker, Residents in Neurology, for the remaining neurological examinations.

A number of staff members of Indiana University Medical Center contributed valuable assistance to this project. The technicians in Dr. Reitan's laboratory administered many of the psychological tests. Mr. Robert Wegner, Administrative Officer of the Institute of Psychiatric Research, was of great help in several phases of the project, particularly in the selection and equipping of the trailer in which normal readers were tested. Mr. Harry Brittain, Research Assistant in the Biostatistics Laboratory of the Institute of Psychiatric Research, put the data in proper form and carried out the arrangements for computer analysis. And Mrs. Julia Lacy, Research Assistant of the Institute of Psychiatric Research, devised the quantitative rules for scoring the various drawings.

Finally, I am indebted to Miss Diane Ferland, and Mrs. Barbara Corballis for typing the manuscript, and to my wife for her patience and reassurance during the most trying stages of preparation.

D. G. Doehring

Contents

Tables

CHAPTER ONE

Background and Outline
of the Study

A child usually begins to read at the age of 5, 6, or 7. Most children acquire this skill without too much difficulty. However, a child who does not make normal progress in learning to read is severely handicapped in almost all aspects of primary education, and has little chance for success in higher education unless his reading problem can be overcome.

Reading difficulty occurs for many reasons. Poor methods of teaching in school or the lack of appropriate stimulation at home can interfere with reading acquisition. Hereditary factors or disorders of pregnancy in the mother may operate to produce deficiencies in abilities essential to reading. Reading problems may occur in conjunction with impaired vision or hearing, emotional disorders, poor health, slowness in the development of spoken language, brain damage, or general mental subnormality. More subtle deficiencies of visual or auditory perception, oral fluency, fine muscular coordination, motivation, or the sequential maturation of complex skills may also be associated with reading difficulty.

Since there is no single cause of reading difficulty, all possible factors must be considered in attempting to understand the conditions underlying any serious reading problem. Sometimes it is readily apparent that a given condition is detrimental to the acquisition of reading, and the amelioration of this condition will often be followed by improvement to a normal level of reading achievement. This can occur when a visual defect is corrected by the wearing of glasses, when a severe emotional disturbance is aided by psychiatric treatment, or when the effects of inadequate teaching are overcome by appropriate remedial training. In certain instances, however, serious reading difficulty occurs with no obvious associated deficits that can be corrected as a means of improving reading acquisition. This type of reading problem is often called *specific reading disability,* or *developmental dyslexia,* and is characterized as severe impairment of reading acquisition in a child who appears to be normal otherwise.

The existence of an apparently isolated deficiency involving an ability so essential to normal intellectual development has captured the interest of many investigators over the past century. The mere occurrence of such a specific disability would indicate the degree to which human abilities can be differentiated and, by inference, the specificity

1

with which the central nervous system can operate. Any further clarification of the conditions underlying this specific disability should increase our understanding of human abilities in general and of the reading process in particular.

The investigation to be described herein was concerned with the extent of nonreading deficit in children with specific reading disability. The primary purposes were to determine the degree of specificity, if any, of the reading disability and to evaluate the observed scope of nonreading deficit in terms of various hypotheses regarding the underlying basis of specific reading disability. Before any further details of the study are given, some relevant background information will be briefly reviewed.

READING DISABILITY AND
INDIVIDUAL DIFFERENCES

Individual differences in ability can be studied from at least two aspects, differences *between* individuals and differences *within* individuals. Differences between individuals often conform to the normal distribution. The majority of individuals tend to be average or near-average in ability, with a decreasing incidence as the extremes of superiority and inferiority are approached. The distribution of reading ability in the total population, as demonstrated by oral reading proficiency, silent reading vocabulary, or silent reading comprehension, should approximate the normal distribution. Reading disability could, therefore, be defined in terms of relative position in a distribution of scores on a reading achievement test, where all individuals whose scores fall below a predetermined cut-off are classified as disabled or retarded readers. A reading disability group defined by such a procedure would include preschool children, beginning readers, adults with inadequate education, and both children and adults with mental retardation, emotional disturbance, and visual impairment, as well as those with overt brain damage and specific reading disability.

To separate individuals with specific reading disability from the total reading disability group defined by differences in reading ability between individuals, differences within individuals must be determined. All abilities other than reading and perhaps a few abilities basic to reading are presumably at a normal or above-normal level in those persons with specific reading disability. The possibility of this type of wide discrepancy among individual abilities has been demonstrated by investigators such as Spearman (1927), Thurstone (1938), and Guilford (1956), who have found that certain classes of ability may vary in a relatively independent manner within an individual. Such findings have, of course, indicated the inadequacy of the single IQ as representative of the many possible configurations of human ability.

Any estimate of the exact number of separate abilities that can be usefully identified would depend in part upon the scope of behavior under consideration. The majority of investigators have restricted themselves to the types of ability that can be assessed with group paper-and-pencil tests. The statistical technique of factor analysis has been used to determine the number of different types of ability required by a given battery of tests, with each class of ability designated as a separate factor. Some factors which have emerged from analysis of group paper-and-pencil tests are verbal comprehension, word fluency, numerical relationships, spatial relationships, associative memory, perceptual speed, and inductive reasoning (Anastasi, 1958). Of these, the factor most explicitly related to reading is verbal comprehension. Guilford (1956) proposed a multidimensional structure of the intellect which could include as many as 120 unique abilities. Of these, the abilities to recognize symbolic units and semantic units are most directly related to reading (Guilford, 1960).

Although there is general agreement as to the tenability of multiple factor theories of human abilities, none of the present theoretical models is sufficiently broad in scope to encompass the varieties of disorder postulated by one authority or another as underlying specific reading disability. Also, the majority of factored test batteries presuppose a certain amount of reading skill for the comprehension of many items in tests of nonreading skills. Despite the present lack of a factor-analyzed test battery suitable for the assessment of specific reading disability, multiple factor theories of human ability can provide a useful theoretical framework for the explanation of specific reading disability. If reading ability is considered to be just one of many abilities that can vary to some extent independently of one another within an individual, then specific reading disability can be categorized as what Anastasi (1958) calls an *extreme asymmetry of talent*. According to this reasoning, specific reading disability would be studied not as a unique disorder, but in the context of other possible patterns of disability such as a specific deficiency in the comprehension of spatial relationships or a specific difficulty in numerical reasoning. Such specific disabilities may, in turn, be evaluated in terms relative to other configurations of ability. For example, the gifted child may tend to show superior aptitude for the majority of skills, while the mentally retarded child is presumably below normal in the majority of abilities. The term *idiot savant* has been applied to cases where a single ability, most commonly for music, mathematics, or drawing, is average or above-average, with a general subnormality of other abilities. This type of asymmetry might be considered the mirror image of a specific disability.

The classification of specific reading disability as one of many possible profiles of individual difference could prove more fruitful as a theoretical rationale than some of the more restricted characterizations of this problem as a unique and isolated disorder. The increased perspective afforded by such an approach should make it more likely that any new findings regarding specific reading disability will be incorporated into the existing body of scientific knowledge regarding reading and human abilities. Many of the earlier studies of reading disability, as reviewed by Vernon (1957) and Critchley (1964), were very narrowly conceived, which probably accounts for the scarcity of scientifically acceptable explanations of reading disability despite the vast number of investigations in this area.

READING DISABILITY AND
CEREBRAL DYSFUNCTION

Specific reading disability can also be considered within the frame of reference of differential changes of ability resulting from localized cerebral dysfunction. Theories which attempt to relate cerebral activity and human abilities have tended to vary from one extreme which identified specific cortical areas with specific intellectual faculties to an opposite extreme which held that the brain functions as an indivisible whole in an indivisibly whole organism (cf. Boring, 1950). Although these traditional explanations of cerebral function possessed the elegance and virtues of simple philosophy, it has become increasingly evident that no simple theory will suffice, and that any workable explanation of the brain and behavior must be formulated at a higher level of complexity.

Since the end of World War II many neuropsychologists, including Halstead (1947), McFie and Piercy (1952), Milner (1962), Reitan (1964), and Teuber (1952), have directed their efforts toward an empirical description of differential changes of ability associated with cerebral lesions rather than toward further attempts to prove or disprove simple theories of cerebral localization or mass action. Although these investigators have not always agreed regarding such matters as the types of brain lesion most suitable for study, the kinds of evidence necessary for valid descriptions of the locus, extent, and type of brain lesion, and the most appropriate analytic techniques for correlating brain lesions with changes in ability, there does seem to be general agreement that certain abilities tend to be selectively impaired by lesions which impinge upon certain regions of the brain. On the basis of such studies (cf. Milner, 1962; Reitan, 1959, 1964, 1965), several generalizations relevant to the concerns of the present investigation can be advanced:

1. Verbal abilities are most severely impaired by lesions of the "dominant" hemisphere. This is the left hemisphere for the majority of right-handed individuals and for about half of left-handed individuals.*
2. Expressive verbal abilities such as speaking and writing tend

---

*Historically, the adjectives "dominant" or "major" have been used to describe the cerebral hemisphere which subserves speech and language functions, and "nondominant" or "minor" to denote the cerebral hemisphere which does not. Since the connotations of these descriptive adjectives may be misleading, in the following discussions it will be assumed unless otherwise stated that the left hemisphere is the one which subserves language functions.

to be more impaired by anterior lesions, and receptive abilities such as listening and reading by posterior lesions of the left hemisphere.

3. Reading ability may be impaired by lesions of the posterior region of the left hemisphere; and this visual verbal disability, which is commonly designated as dyslexia, tends to occur in conjunction with other deficits of visual and verbal ability.

4. Certain nonverbal abilities tend to be most severely impaired by lesions of the "nondominant" hemisphere. This is the right hemisphere for most right-handed individuals and for about half of left-handed individuals. These abilities usually involve the manipulation or construction of nonverbal forms or spatial arrays.

5. Sensory and motor abilities of the right side of the body tend to be more impaired by lesions of the left hemisphere, and abilities of the left side by lesions of the right hemisphere. Relatively simple skills involving speed and strength of hand movement tend to be more impaired by lesions of the anterior region of the hemisphere opposite to the affected hand, and certain complex skills tend to be more impaired by posterior lesions of this hemisphere.

If specific reading disability is actually the result of localized cerebral dysfunction, and if this presumably congenital condition in children has effects similar to those of acquired brain lesions in adults, then reading disability should tend to occur in association with dysfunction of the posterior region of the left hemisphere. If such is the case, other visual and verbal disabilities may occur in conjunction with reading disability, and there may be some impairment of the functioning of the right hand. It should be noted, however, that dyslexia in an adult constitutes the loss of a previously acquired ability, whereas in specific reading disability or congenital dyslexia the reading problem is almost always evident from the time the child begins to learn to read.

The empirical findings of neuropsychologists must be regarded as providing a useful framework for speculations regarding a possible neurological basis of specific reading disability. Within this framework certain predictions regarding the expected pattern of nonreading deficit can be made, as specified in the paragraph above. These predictions are made by analogy to the effects of acquired brain lesions in adults, since direct evidence regarding the effects of verified cerebral lesions in children is very sparse (Benton, 1962). The joint contexts of individual differences and cerebral dysfunction should serve to provide an interesting basis for predictions regarding the configuration of nonreading deficit which may accompany specific reading disability.

READING DISABILITY
AND APHASIA

The term *aphasia* is customarily used to denote language disorders resulting from acquired cerebral dysfunction. Although the exact definition of this term has been fraught with ambiguity, many writers would classify practically all forms of verbal impairment produced by brain damage as aphasia. There has been very little agreement, nonetheless, regarding the degree to which language abilities may be selectively impaired by localized cortical lesions. Theories of aphasia, in a manner quite similar to theories of cortical function in general, have fluctuated between those which postulated the association of specific language faculties with specific locations in the cerebral cortex, and those which postulated that the mass action of the brain would preclude any specific impairment of language abilities. The historical background and current theories of aphasia have been reviewed recently by several writers (Brain, 1961; Osgood and Miron, 1963; Schuell, Jenkins, and Jimenez-Pabon, 1964).

The preceding discussion of the effects of cerebral dysfunction has a direct bearing on the present topic, since reading must be classified as a language ability, and aphasia encompasses all forms of language impairment resulting from cerebral dysfunction. Furthermore, the empirical findings of neuropsychologists are in accordance with current explanations of the types of cerebral dysfunction associated with aphasia. Aphasia tends to occur only after lesions involving certain areas of the left hemisphere; disturbances of speech and writing tend to occur with anterior lesions and disturbances of listening and reading with posterior lesions; and many aphasic patients have hemiparesis (partial paralysis) of the right side of the body. Thus, the consideration of reading disability in the frame of reference of aphasia merely represents a slight change of emphasis. "Aphasiologists," as Critchley (1964) calls them, are primarily interested in language impairment resulting from brain damage, whereas neuropsychologists are interested in both language and nonlanguage effects of cerebral dysfunction. This probably reflects the orientation of aphasiologists toward treatment, in contrast to the orientation of most neuropsychologists toward description of the brain-behavior relationship.

Acquired reading disorders manifested by patients classified as aphasic are usually designated by the terms dyslexia or word-blindness. Of interest here is the question of whether dyslexia may appear as an isolated disorder and, if so, whether this disorder is thought to result from a focal cortical lesion. Not unexpectedly, viewpoints in this matter have ranged from extreme localization theories to mass action theories. In 1872 Broadbent first described dyslexia as an aphasic disorder and localized the disorder to the angular and supramarginal gyri located in the posterior region of the left hemisphere (Critchley, 1964). Many of the later discussions of "pure" dyslexia also implicate this same region and present autopsy findings for individuals who were said to have manifested pure word-blindness. There has been an equal weight of opinion against the possible existence of pure dyslexia among eminent neurologists such as Head (1926), who leaned more in the direction of mass action theories.

More recently, Geschwind (1962) proposed a very interesting explanation of pure word-blindness. He said that it is possible for acquired reading disability to occur in isolation in cases where there is joint occurrence of a lesion of the visual area in the posterior region of the left hemisphere and a lesion of the splenium of the corpus callosum, the commisure which connects the two cerebral hemispheres; and that both types of lesion could result from occlusion of the posterior cerebral artery. Pure word-blindness, therefore, could conceivably occur as a result of cerebral vascular disorder.

Another extreme of contemporary opinion is represented by Schuell and Jenkins (1959), whose extensive investigations of aphasic adults suggested a unitary dimension of language deficit in aphasia, with no indication of independent language functions. However, these writers do not favor a complete mass action theory of language impairment. In a later publication (Schuell, Jenkins, and Jimenez-Pabon, 1964) they differentiate five categories of aphasic disorder, with the category most pertinent to reading designated as aphasia complicated by central involvement of visual processes.

Within the frame of reference of aphasia, specific reading disability can be compared to acquired dyslexia or word-blindness in adults. Some writers have suggested that pure word-blindness can occur as an isolated disorder produced by localized cortical lesions, while others feel that acquired reading disorders can occur only in conjunction with a relatively broad spectrum of other language disorders. Some of the earliest explanations of specific reading disability stemmed directly from the localization theories, as will be seen below.

THE ORIGIN OF SPECIFIC
READING DISABILITY

In the preceding sections specific reading disability was discussed in the contexts of individual differences, cerebral dysfunction, and aphasia. Other contexts of less direct relevance, such as personality factors, teaching methods, and sociocultural circumstances have been considered elsewhere (Harris, 1961; Johnson, 1957; Money, 1962; Vernon, 1957). Many different explanations of specific reading disability have been proposed. A complete survey of these is not within the scope of this report. The following discussion will be largely concerned with those theories that are most pertinent to the interpretation of the present study. The majority bear some relationship to factors discussed in the preceding sections.

Congenital Word-Blindness

Just before the beginning of the twentieth century an English school doctor named James Kerr called attention to severe reading problems in children who seemed to have no other intellectual defects. Shortly thereafter another English physician, W. Pringle Morgan, described a case of "congenital word-blindness" in a 14 year old boy of normal intelligence (Hermann, 1959). Morgan suggested that the disorder might be the result of a deficiency in the development of the left angular gyrus.

A much more thorough description of congenital word-blindness was published in 1917 by James Hinshelwood, a Glasgow ophthalmologist (Hinshelwood, 1917). He also attributed specific reading difficulty to underdevelopment of the left angular gyrus, and he considered this area of the dominant hemisphere to be a storehouse for visual memory images of words and letters. However, neither Hinshelwood nor any subsequent proponents of this theory presented any direct evidence for lesions of the angular gyrus in cases of congenital word-blindness. Hinshelwood's reasoning in this regard was that congenital word-blindness must result from a cortical defect because of the intractibility of the reading problem, and this cortical defect must be congenital because of the lack of any history of acquired cortical lesions (Critchley, 1964; Hermann, 1959; Vernon, 1957).

This explanation of congenital word-blindness in terms of agenesis of the left angular gyrus was derived from a direct analogy to the localization theories of acquired aphasia. Other terms that have been used to denote this viewpoint regarding the origin of specific reading disability are constitutional dyslexia, congenital symbol-amblyopia, congenital typholexia, bradylexia, analfabetia partialis, and amnesia visualis verbalis (Drew, 1956).

Strephosymbolia

Another well-known explanation of specific reading disorders was formulated by Samuel T. Orton, an American neuropsychiatrist (Orton, 1937). He agreed with Hinshelwood that reading disability was a defect of visual perception produced by dysfunction of the left cerebral hemisphere, but stated that the major causative factor was a failure to develop cerebral dominance. According to Orton, when a child learns to read, "engrams" or "traces" of the printed words are formed in both cerebral hemispheres. The traces formed in the nondominant hemisphere are the mirror image of those formed in the dominant hemisphere. A specific reading disorder which he named "strephosymbolia" was said to occur when the reversed traces in the nondominant hemisphere are inadequately suppressed by the dominant hemisphere because of delayed or incomplete development of cerebral dominance. Strephosymbolia was said to be characterized by reversal of letters and words in reading and by "mirror writing," and accompanied by inconsistencies of hand, eye, and foot preference.

Orton's theory has been largely discredited, partly because of the difficulty of testing its neurological propositions and partly because the patterns of reading, spelling, and writing errors observed in children with specific reading disability cannot be explained very adequately in terms of a confusion of mirror images (Tomkins, 1963; Vernon, 1957). However, the association of mixed hand, eye, and foot preferences in children with specific reading disability still appears to be widely accepted (Critchley, 1964).

Hereditary Factors

Reading problems can be classified as congenital where there is evidence of an inherited, genetically transmitted disorder, and also where the disorder is shown to be associated with abnormal circumstances of pregnancy and delivery. The most extensive investigation of a possible hereditary factor in reading disability was conducted in Sweden by Hallgren (1950). He reported a primary and a secondary form of specific dyslexia, with the primary form said to be inherited as a unitary Mendelian dominant characteristic. It is probably best, as Vernon (1957) suggests, to await further corroborative evidence that a certain form of specific reading disability can be inherited as a simple genetic factor. A theory of congenital word-blindness such as that of Hinshelwood would, of course, assume some form of hereditary transmission.

Prenatal and Perinatal Factors

Kawi and Pasamanick (1959) found that specific reading disability can result from disorders of pregnancy and delivery. They had hypothesized that certain reading problems might be attributable to minimal brain damage produced by abnormalities of the prenatal and perinatal periods. This was part of a more general hypothesis that there is a "continuum of reproductive casualty" extending from fetal death through a descending gradient of brain damage to relatively mild, selective disturbances of behavior. Although there is little doubt that many reading problems are associated with prenatal and perinatal disorders, the exact manner in which the supposed structural impairment interferes with reading acquisition has not yet been determined.

Directional Confusion and Gerstmann's Syndrome

Knud Hermann (1959), a Danish neurologist, proposed that the fundamental disorder in congenital reading disability was directional confusion or right-left disorientation. This disturbance of lateral orientation relative to the body schema was said to interfere with reading acquisition by producing errors such as reversal, rotation, and disfigurement of visual symbols. Hermann considered this underdevelopment of directional function to be a specific, inherited factor in congenital reading disability. He further related directional confusion to Gerstmann's Syndrome, a constellation of four symptoms (disturbances of calculational ability, finger localization, writing, and right-left orientation) usually associated with lesions of the dominant cerebral hemisphere in the region of the angular gyrus. Although the incidence of right-left disorientation in children with reading disability can be easily assessed, the hypothesized causal relationship would be more difficult to confirm. Hermann's suggested inclusion of the remaining symptoms of Gerstmann's syndrome represents a modification of the usual neurological analogy to "pure" dyslexia.

Neurochemical Factors

Smith and Carrigan (1959) embarked upon a completely different tack in proposing that reading disability results from a disturbance of synaptic transmission involving abnormal modes of action of the neurochemical substances acetylcholine and cholinesterase. Although this explanation has a certain amount of face validity (a higher-than-normal incidence of endocrine disorders was found in a group of children with reading disability), no direct connection between neurochemical transmission and reading disability was demonstrated in the investigations reported by Smith and Carrigan. However, the continuing increase of interest in the neurochemistry of learning (cf. Gaito and Zavala, 1964) may eventually result in a more convincing demonstration of the role of neurochemical factors in reading disability.

Gestalt Disturbances of Visuo-Motor Functioning

Explanations of reading disability and other learning disorders of childhood in terms of immaturity or disturbance in "visuo-motor," "perceptuo-motor," or "visual-motor" functioning have become quite popular in recent years. This viewpoint has been most thoroughly developed by de Hirsch (1954). In her extensive work with language-impaired children she has used the Bender Gestalt Test (Bender, 1938) as the main criterion of visuo-motor disturbance and has found this test to reveal a striking immaturity of "Gestalt functioning" in children classified as dyslexic. Gestalt disturbance is characterized by difficulty in synthesizing visual configurations, difficulty in experiencing spatial and temporal relationships, primitive body image, impairment of figure-background relationships, difficulty in responding to a constellation of stimuli as a whole, difficulty in the orderly recall of sequences, deficiencies of temporal structuralization, and difficulty in the patterning of fine motor coordination. These problems are said to occur not only in perceptual and motor performance, but also at every level of integration and organization of behavior. As a consequence, dyslexic children are said to have trouble inhibiting and channelling impulses, which results in an inability to organize the endless stream of stimuli into behavioral configurations. The cerebral region involved in this type of disturbance might well be the reticular formation rather than the dominant angular gyrus (cf. Jasper et al., 1958).

Explanations such as tnose of de Hirsch which invoke visuo-motor Gestalt disturbances may provide valuable suggestions for treatment, but as theories they are difficult either to prove or disprove by direct empirical tests of specific propositions. It seems entirely possible that such a diffuse disturbance of function would produce a disorder much more widespread than specific reading disability. Lachmann (1960) found visuo-motor disturbances on the Bender Gestalt Test not only in retarded readers, but also in normal readers with emotional disturbance. However, de Hirsch herself has made great strides toward empirical verification by assembling a group of tests, including the Bender Gestalt, for predicting later reading difficulty in children of kindergarten age (de Hirsch, 1955; 1957). This type of longitudinal investigation should be of great value toward the further understanding of specific reading disability.

Maturation of Perceptual Abilities

Birch (1962) described 3 aspects of perceptual maturation which could be relevant to the explanation of specific reading disability. First, it can be hypothesized that sensory systems develop in a certain sequence, with an initial predominance of tactual-kinesthetic sensitivity succeeded by a later dominance of the distance sensory systems of vision and hearing. Where vision and hearing do not become dominant in a normal manner the child may not be ready to learn to read at the time he enters school. Second, as these sensory systems are developed the child learns to respond in an equivalent manner to different channels of sensory input, for example the sight, sound, and smell of food cooking. A deficiency in the development of abilities related to intersensory equivalence could directly interfere with acquisition of the visual equivalents of spoken words and letters. Third, the development of perceptual abilities may take the form of an increase in complexity from an early level of simple discrimination through the ability to analyze and finally to synthesize complex stimuli. Reading disability could result from inadequate development of these higher levels of visual perception.

Although the first and the third aspects of maturation described by Birch might produce intellectual deficiencies much too widespread to be termed specific reading disability, it seems entirely possible that specific reading disability could be the result of some abnormality of perceptual maturation.

ASSOCIATED DEFICIENCIES
OF NONREADING ABILITIES

Several kinds of nonreading deficit were cited in connection with the preceding discussion of the origin of specific reading disability. These included inconsistency of hand and eye dominance; directional confusion or right-left disorientation; disturbances of calculation ability, finger localization, and writing; Gestalt disturbances of visual-motor functioning; and delayed maturation of perceptual abilities. Some other pertinent findings regarding nonreading deficit in specific reading disability are summarized below.

Rabinovitch *et al.* (1954) used the term *primary reading retardation* to describe cases of reading disability with no gross neurological deficit, personality disorder, or educational handicap. They felt that primary reading retardation was one aspect of a larger disturbance of integration, and resulted from a developmental discrepancy. Nonreading deficits found to be associated with primary reading retardation were low Verbal IQ relative to Performance IQ on the WISC (Wechsler Intelligence Scale for Children), right-left confusion, sensory inattention or extinction phenomena in response to double simultaneous stimulation, mixed hand-eye dominance, nonspecific motor awkwardness, speech abnormalities, and writing abnormalities. However, they pointed out that few if any patients exhibited all of these deficits.

Drew (1956) examined 3 cases of familial dyslexia and concluded that inconsistencies of nonreading deficit among these cases were attributable to a common defect of Gestalt functions expressed as disturbances in intra- and extra-personal spatial perception.

Myklebust and Johnson (1962) reviewed 200 cases classified as childhood dyslexia and described the following syndrome of nonreading deficit: disturbance of orientation, topographic disorder (difficulty in spatial symbolization), dyschronometria (difficulty in learning sequences and temporal relationships), inability to write, spelling disability, calculational difficulty, difficulty in learning foreign languages, memory disorders, inability to auditorize or to visualize, subtle motor disorders, and neurological disturbances.

Silver and Hagin (1960) reported a study of 150 children with reading disability who showed nonreading deficits in right-left orientation, visual-motor disturbances on the Bender Gestalt Test, visual figure-background disturbance on the Marble Board Test, difficulty in certain aspects of auditory discrimination, and disturbance of body-image schema on the Draw-a-Person Test. Not all of these defects occurred in all children with reading disability. In a follow-up study of 24 cases, Silver and Hagin (1964) found that the disturbances of right-left orientation and auditory discrimination had disappeared, and visual-motor, visual figure-background, and body-schema disturbances had diminished in scope relative to the performance of a control group of normal readers.

In a study of 12 cases of reading disability Shankweiler (1964) found nonreading deficits involving directional confusion and difficulties in drawing and copying. Belmont and Birch (1965) found a significant amount of right-left confusion in a sample of 150 poor readers. Several investigators (Graham and Kamano, 1958; Neville, 1961; Robeck, 1960; Sheldon and Garton, 1959) have found deficiencies on certain subtests of the various Wechsler intelligence tests in children with reading problems. It should also be noted that some investigators have failed to find inconsistencies of hand and eye dominance despite careful evaluation of lateral dominance (Belmont and Birch, 1965; Silver and Hagin, 1960; Spitzer, Rabkin, and Kramer, 1959).

Critical Evaluation of Nonreading Deficit

The significance of nonreading deficiencies in children with specific reading disability must be interpreted with care. Critchley (1964) has pointed out that certain associated symptoms may occur with a higher-than-normal incidence in developmental dyslexia, and yet still have no intrinsic association with the reading problem. Similarly, Shankweiler (1964) mentions that the demonstration of a correlation between a given nonreading deficit and reading disability does not necessarily prove that the deficit has interfered with the process of learning to read.

A nonreading deficit should be evaluated by comparison with the incidence of this deficit among normal readers whenever possible. And the possible significance of a nonreading deficit must also be considered in terms of its frequency of occurrence in relation to the occurrence or nonoccurrence of other nonreading deficits.

Finally, the disorder itself must be clearly defined in order that any associated deficit can be interpreted unambiguously. There can, of course, be several different, clearly defined populations of children with specific reading disability. Belmont and Birch (1965), whose sample was selected from a total school population, are almost certainly not dealing with exactly the same reading disorder as the neurologist who sees cases referred to him in the setting of clinical medicine. Critchley (1964) makes a very explicit distinction in this regard by listing the premises of developmental dyslexia as persistence into adulthood, certain specific peculiarities of reading and writing errors, familial incidence, and associated symbolic defects. He states that this condition is relatively rare, and includes only a small proportion of poor readers.

In our present state of knowledge there is no unequivocal basis for choice among the various definitions of specific reading disability, theories as to its origin, and tabulations of associated nonreading deficit. It does behoove the investigator in this area to support any new findings regarding specific reading disability by precise description of the methods used to select and evaluate the particular population under consideration. To this end, an attempt has been made to describe the investigative procedures of the study to be reported here as explicitly as possible within the confines of necessary brevity.

OUTLINE OF THE STUDY

The possible value of a thorough assessment of the nonreading abilities of children with specific reading disability became apparent to the writer during a year spent at the Neuropsychology Laboratory of the Indiana University Medical Center. The objective tests and the precise analytic methods developed by neuropsychologists to identify the patterns of behavioral deficit associated with cerebral dysfunction in adults seemed almost equally appropriate for evaluation of the patterns of behavioral deficit associated with an extreme asymmetry of ability in school-age children.

A colleague, Hallgrim Kløve, had assembled a preliminary group of children referred for testing to the Neuropsychology Laboratory with a tentative diagnosis of specific reading disability. The most consistent finding was a tendency for Verbal IQ on the Wechsler-Bellevue Intelligence Scale to be much lower than Performance IQ. Otherwise, there were indications of impairment on certain tests that had been found to be sensitive to acquired brain damage in adults. However, these findings were not always clear. Exact interpretation was difficult because the diagnosis of specific reading disability was sometimes open to question and because there were insufficient normative data for school-age children.

The above considerations ultimately resulted in a decision to administer a more elaborate battery of tests to a group of children especially selected on the basis of objective criteria of specific reading disability, and to assess the pattern of nonreading deficit in these children by comparison of their test performance with that of a group of normal readers matched in age, educational opportunity, and Performance IQ. The battery of neuropsychological tests was elaborated for the purposes of providing a more thorough survey of abilities possibly relevant to the reading deficit and at the same time to assess as many as possible of the types of ability that have been said by previous theorists to underly specific reading disability. For the selection of children with specific reading disability, a stringent set of criteria was applied in order to minimize any ambiguity regarding the definition of the disorder. A child was judged as having a specific reading disability if he had a normal nonverbal IQ but was severely retarded in reading. No evidence of hereditary transmission was required, and evidence of prenatal, perinatal, or postnatal cerebral trauma was not grounds for exclusion. It should be noted at the outset that these criteria were broader than those recommended by previous writers such as Critchley (1964).

In addition to the battery of tests, most of the children were given a standard neurological examination, and standard medical and developmental histories as well as a history of familial reading disorders were obtained for all children. A total of 67 children with specific reading problems were tested. The majority were obtained through remedial reading programs. From these a group of 39 boys was selected who met the criteria of specific reading disability. Then a group of children with no reading problems was tested, and from this a group of 39 boys and a group of 39 girls were selected to match the reading disability group in age and Performance IQ. The group of boys was used for the majority of comparisons with retarded readers.

Patterns of nonreading deficit were assessed in several ways: (1) For each test, the mean score of the reading disability group was statistically compared with that of the normal readers, and the extent of nonreading deficit was described in terms of the number of tests on which the mean of the normal readers significantly exceeded the mean of the retarded readers; (2) a separate factor analysis was performed for the test results of each group, and the composition of the resulting factors was examined as another means of identifying differences in the configuration of abilities of children with specific reading disability; (3) the statistical techniques of multiple stepwise regression and discriminant analysis were used to determine the sets of nonreading measures which best differentiated normal readers from retarded readers; (4) the individual test profiles of a subsample of retarded readers were analyzed in detail to determine whether the nonreading deficit of the group tended to be consistently reflected in individual cases; and (5) the individual test results of normal and retarded readers were evaluated separately by Ralph Reitan and Hallgrim Kløve, who estimated the probability of cerebral dysfunction in each case by means of an impressionistic analytic technique developed in the Neuropsychology Laboratory. In addition to the analyses of test results, the neurological and case history findings were evaluated by A. L. Drew as a means of assessing the neurological evidence for cerebral dysfunction.

It was hoped that the results of this study would clearly delineate and differentiate areas of normality and areas of subnormality in the configuration of abilities of children with specific reading disability, and that the interpretation of the observed configurations would contribute to a further understanding of specific reading disability and other asymmetries of talent in children.

This research was carried out under the auspices of the Institute of Psychiatric Research, the Neuropsychology Laboratory, and the Department of Neurology of the Indiana University Medical Center. A great deal of the testing, interviewing of parents, and compilation of data was done by Mrs. Ann Fuller. The experimental plan was devised in collaboration with A. L. Drew, Ralph Reitan, and Hallgrim Kløve. Most of the neurological examinations were carried out by Caridad Cruz. Statistical analyses were accomplished in collaboration with James Norton. A large part of the rationale for interpreting the results of this study was derived from the work of Reitan and his associates.

CHAPTER TWO

Subjects Studied: Criteria for Selection

RETARDED READERS

The criteria used to select children with specific reading disability are described below. For convenience and clarity, the children who met these criteria will be designated as Retarded Readers. This term is meant to imply a well-verified retardation of reading with no positive evidence of any other retardation or abnormality except for the deficiencies of educational achievement that unavoidably result from reading retardation.

Children with reading problems were referred to us from several different sources, including the Reading Clinic of the Indianapolis Public Schools, the Remedial Reading Program of the Indianapolis Parochial Schools, a private reading clinic in Indianapolis, and through direct referrals to the Neuropsychology Laboratory. The public school reading clinic accepted only those children whose measured IQ was above 90 and whose educational problem seemed to be specifically related to reading. All of the 26 boys and 1 girl obtained from this clinic had been adjudged to have severe specific reading problems. The remedial reading program of the parochial schools attempted to help as many retarded readers as possible by the use of trained volunteers within the school situation. All of the 19 boys and 1 girl obtained from this source had scored above 90 on a group intelligence test. The privately operated reading clinic provided individual tutoring for children with reading problems. All 5 of the boys obtained through this clinic were adjudged to have severe specific reading defects on the basis of a variety of diagnostic procedures. Finally, 12 boys and 3 girls were obtained through direct referral to the Neuropsychology Laboratory. The major complaint in these cases involved poor reading.

From the 67 children with reading problems who were tested, 39 boys met the criteria of reading retardation described below. This group consisted of 22 boys from the public school reading clinic, 13 from the parochial school remedial reading program, 3 from the private reading clinic, and one from the Neuropsychology Laboratory. Included in the group were 4 pairs of brothers, one pair of whom were fraternal twins.

Of the 28 children who did not meet the criteria, 9 were eliminated because they were not sufficiently retarded in reading achievement, 6 because their nonverbal IQ was below 90, 5 because they fell outside the age limits, 4 because of possible practice effect from having been

given some of the tests on previous occasions, one because of possible
environmental deprivation, one because of gross mental retardation,
and one because of poor vision. Since only one girl met all of the criteria for reading retardation, she was eliminated in order to make the
group homogeneous with respect to sex. Although previous investigators have found specific reading disability to be much commoner
among males (cf. Critchley, 1964), the 39 to 1 ratio in the present study
was unusually high.

In addition to the specific criteria described below, the analysis of
case history information in a later chapter will provide the reader with
a further basis for judging some of the relatively indefinite criteria.

Age

Only children within the age range of 10 through 14 were included.
There were several reasons for this restriction: (1) By the age of 10 a
child has had sufficient educational opportunity to be reliably classified
as a retarded reader; (2) a restriction of age range reduces variability
associated with maturation; (3) this age range was appropriate to a
particular battery of tests used in the Neuropsychology Laboratory; and
(4) an adequate sample of children in this age range was available for
testing. Even with this restriction of age range the 5 age levels cannot
be considered comparable, since the adolescent growth spurt occurs
during this period. For this reason the Retarded Readers and Normal
Readers were carefully matched in age, as described below.

Reading Retardation

Reading retardation was defined in terms of Reading Grade Level
on the Wide Range Achievement Test (Jastak, 1946). This provided a
standardized measure of oral reading ability for single words. The
criterion for reading retardation was a reading level 2 or more years
below the school grade in which the child would be if he had made
normal educational progress. This expected school grade was determined by the number of years the child had been in school since beginning first grade. The actual grade level at the time of testing was
not used to determine reading retardation because several of the children had repeated one or more grades as a direct result of their reading difficulty.

This criterion was probably sufficient as an indication of severe
reading retardation for the present group, since all of the children had
been given remedial instruction. The combined reading and intelligence
criteria (see below) conform to the recommendation of Rabinovitch *et al*
(1954) that the diagnosis of reading retardation should be made when
reading ability is 2 years below a child's mental age as determined by
the performance scale of a standard intelligence test. Finally, the test
of oral word reading ability, which could be defined as a measure of
oral phonetic symbolization, provided a quantitative estimate of overall

reading retardation. Tests of more complex silent reading skills such as word meaning and paragraph comprehension would probably have shown an equivalent or greater retardation in this group of retarded readers.

Explicit Reading Complaint

In each case the reading problem had been originally identified on the basis of complaints from teachers and parents that a difficulty in reading was seriously impeding the child's educational progress. This is an important defining characteristic, since a group such as this would not necessarily have the same characteristics as a group selected from an entire school system to include all children within the normal intelligence range who happened to be 2 years retarded in oral word reading.

Normal Performance IQ

Before reading retardation can be defined as a specific disability, some criterion must be postulated for the elimination of children whose reading retardation is merely one aspect of general mental subnormality. Therefore, all definitions of specific reading disability must specify a discrepancy between reading ability and other abilities. In his choice of a criterion the investigator must hazard a guess as to what abilities are directly involved in the deficit of reading acquisition, and then assess "otherwise normal intelligence" on the basis of a representative sample of abilities which are presumably neither basic to the reading deficit nor secondarily impaired by it.

The estimate of intelligence chosen for the present study was Performance IQ on the Wechsler-Bellevue Scale (Wechsler, 1944). To qualify as a retarded reader a child was required to have a Performance IQ of at least 90; that is, either within or above the normal range of nonverbal intelligence. The results of the present study, to be discussed in a later chapter, indicated that even this restricted criterion of intelligence may have included an ability basic to the reading deficit.

Normal Psychiatric Status

There were no current or past psychiatric disorders among the Retarded Readers. In almost every case the child was quite concerned about his reading problem and expressed feelings of inadequacy regarding his poor educational achievement. Indeed, such a reaction is probably more realistic than a bland acceptance of the problem.

Although a careful assessment of personality variables by a standard interview or by standardized tests might have been desirable, such procedures were not feasible. The cooperation of parents and school officials was obtained with the understanding that no projective test or other methods of personality assessment would be used. It is possible, therefore, that although there were no cases of overt psychiatric disturbance, the Retarded Readers may have differed from the control group of normal readers in some aspects of personal adjustment.

Normal Educational Opportunity

All of the children had begun school at the normal age and had been taught by conventional methods under ordinary circumstances. None had a history of unusually lengthy absence from school as a result of illness, or for any other reason.

Normal Home Environment

All of the children had been raised under normal circumstances within the general sociocultural environment of the white middle class in the midwestern section of the United States.

Normal Vision and Hearing

None of the children had defects of hearing or uncorrected visual defects of clinical significance. Although these primary sensory abilities were not directly tested as part of this study, in all cases where there had been any question of visual or auditory impairment the absence of such impairment had been confirmed by prior examination.

Normal Health

All children were normal in general health. There were no cases of gross defects of motor function or coordination that would interfere with speech, writing, or visual-motor skills.

Summary

The group of Retarded Readers consisted of 39 boys between the ages of 10 and 14, with retardation in oral reading ability of 2 years or more despite remedial reading instruction, a specific complaint regarding the reading problem, Performance IQ of 90 or above, normal psychiatric status, normal educational opportunity, normal home environment, normal vision and hearing, and normal health and motor function.

It should be noted that some factors were not restricted by criteria of selection, but were allowed to vary freely. These included verbal abilities, language development, methods by which reading had been taught, and neurological status, except as these factors might affect the criterion variables. Other investigators might well define reading disability as even more specific by requiring normal verbal ability and neurological status in addition to the criteria used in the present study.

NORMAL READERS

The ability of Retarded Readers was assessed by comparison of their test performance with that of a group of normal readers. An ideal control group would consist of children not retarded in reading acquisition and who did not differ from the Retarded Readers in any of the other criteria listed above. Such an ideal could not be fully realized because of the difficulty of obtaining children who were demonstrably the same as the Retarded Readers in educational opportunity and home environment. A common procedure for equating 2 groups in educational opportunity and home environment is to select both groups from the same school or schools. This was not possible in the present study. The control group was obtained by a procedure which permitted precise control of age, reading status, and Performance IQ, but with a less ideal control of educational opportunity and home environment.

Permission was obtained to select a group of normal readers from the total school populations of Fall Creek Heights Elementary School and Markleville High School, both located outside of Anderson, Indiana. The tests were administered in a trailer parked outside Fall Creek Heights School, with children transported from Markleville High School during school hours for testing. Since this arrangement eliminated the necessity of parents bringing their children in for testing, we were able to test almost all of the children who were initially selected.

A total of 49 boys in the age range of 10 through 14 were tested, of whom 42 attended the elementary school and 7 attended the high school. From these, a group of 39 boys was selected whose reading ability was normal and who were equivalent to the Retarded Readers in age and Performance IQ. The group included 3 pairs of brothers, none of whom were twins.

In connection with a program for the collection of normative data for the Neuropsychology Laboratory, 48 girls from Fall Creek Heights and Markleville Schools were also tested. Of these, a group of 39 girls was selected who were normal readers and who matched the boys in age and in Performance IQ. Several limited comparisons of this group with Retarded Readers will be presented.

Age

Table 1 shows the distribution of age in all 3 groups. The groups were well matched in this respect. The mean age of Retarded Readers was 5 months greater than that of the Male and Female Normal Readers. If anything, this difference would tend to decrease the observed magnitude of any deficiency of the Retarded Readers.

Reading Retardation

Reading retardation was calculated by determining a child's expected school grade (the grade in which he would be if he had made

TABLE 1

Distribution of age in Retarded Readers, Male Normal Readers, and Female Normal Readers

AGE	FREQUENCY		
	RETARDED READERS	MALE NORMAL	FEMALE NORMAL
10 - 1 to 10 - 3	1	1	1
10 - 4 10 - 6	3	2	4
10 - 7 10 - 9	2	1	1
10 - 10 11 - 0	1	0	2
11 - 1 to 11 - 3	0	2	1
11 - 4 11 - 6	1	1	1
11 - 7 11 - 9	2	3	1
11 - 10 12 - 0	1	1	1
12 - 1 to 12 - 3	1	1	2
12 - 4 12 - 6	0	2	2
12 - 7 12 - 9	3	3	0
12 - 10 13 - 0	2	2	2
13 - 1 to 13 - 3	3	4	2
13 - 4 13 - 6	2	1	4
13 - 7 13 - 9	4	3	3
13 - 10 14 - 0	3	2	1
14 - 1 to 14 - 3	4	3	1
14 - 4 14 - 6	3	2	1
14 - 7 14 - 9	3	3	5
14 - 10 15 - 0	0	2	4
TOTAL	39	39	39
MEAN	13-4	12-11	12-11

normal educational progress since entering school) at the time of testing to the nearest tenth of a school year and subtracting this from his reading level on the Wide Range Achievement Test, also to the nearest tenth of a school year. Table 2 shows the distribution of reading retardation in each group. None of the Retarded Readers were retarded by less than 2.0 years, with the majority retarded by 3, 4, or 5 years. None of the Normal Readers were retarded by more than 1.0 year. About one fourth of the Male and Female Normal Reader groups were retarded by one half to one year, with the average in each group falling above the zero point of reading retardation. Although it might have been preferable to eliminate all children with any retardation in reading achievement from the Normal Reader groups, this could not have been accomplished without reducing the precision of other criteria upon which the groups were equated. If anything, the inclusion of children with up to one year of reading retardation in the Normal Reader groups should tend to attenuate any deficiency in the Retarded Readers.

TABLE 2

Distribution of retardation in reading achievement on the Wide Range Achievement Test. No member of the Retarded Reading Group was retarded by less than 2.0 years, and no member of the Male or Female Normal Reading Groups was retarded by more than 1.0 years.

READING RETARDATION TO NEAREST YEAR	FREQUENCY		
	RETARDED READERS	*MALE NORMAL*	*FEMALE NORMAL*
-5			1
-4			1
-3		2	2
-2		4	5
-1		7	11
0		16	10
1		10	9
2	2		
3	10		
4	14		
5	8		
6	3		
7			
8	2		
TOTAL	39	39	39
MEAN	4.2	-0.3	-0.7

Explicit Reading Complaint

There had been no explicit complaints regarding reading acquisition for any children in the Normal Reading groups, and none had been given remedial reading instruction.

Intelligence

Table 3 shows the distribution of Performance IQ for each group. Over 60 percent of the Retarded Readers fell within the normal range of 90 to 110, with the remainder falling within the range 110 to 130. In order to equate the groups in mean Performance IQ it was necessary to include several children with IQ's in the 85-89 range in the Normal Reading groups. Otherwise the IQ distributions were very well matched.

Normal Psychiatric Status, Educational Opportunity, Home Environment, Vision and Hearing, General Health

In all of the above respects the conditions of normalcy for the Normal Reading groups were the same as those stated above for the

TABLE 3

Distribution of Performance IQ on the Wechsler-Bellevue Scale. IQs
in the below-90 category were 86 and 89 in the Male Normal Reader
group and 87, 88, and 88 in the Female Normal Reader group. IQs
130 and above were 130 in the Male Normal and 132 in the Female
Normal group.

		FREQUENCY	
PERFORMANCE IQ	RETARDED READERS	MALE NORMAL	FEMALE NORMAL
Below 90		2	3
90–99	12	8	6
100–109	12	13	11
110–119	9	9	12
120–129	6	6	6
130 & above		1	1
TOTAL	39	39	39
MEAN	107.0	106.8	108.5

Retarded Readers. However, the home and school environment of the
Retarded Readers was urban-suburban in contrast to the suburban-
rural environment of the Normal Readers. Although such a difference
of background could conceivably have some systematic influence on
certain abilities, the differences between groups that were actually observed could hardly be explained by a bias of this sort.

Summary

A group of 39 boys and a group of 39 girls designated as Normal
Readers were matched with 39 Retarded Readers in age and Performance IQ. The Normal Readers were within the normal range of oral
reading achievement and had no history of reading difficulty. All
groups were normal in psychiatric status, educational opportunity,
home environment, vision and hearing, and general health.

CHAPTER THREE

Tests, Case History Interview, and Neurological Examination

Most of the quantified measures used for comparison of the abilities of Normal and Retarded Readers were obtained from the test battery developed for ages 10 to 14 at the Indiana University Neuropsychology Laboratory, and from a modification of the Minnesota Test for Differential Diagnosis of Aphasia (Research Edition: Form 7). These measures, along with those obtained from a small number of other psychological tests, constituted the basic data of the present study. In addition, all of the Retarded Readers and over half of the Normal Readers were given a neurological examination, and detailed case history information was secured by means of an interview with parents of all but a few of the children.

TESTS

The entire set of tests yielded 109 measures for use in the statistical comparison of groups. Each measure is briefly described in Appendix A (p. 151), where mention is also made of a number of items from the Halstead-Wepman Aphasia Screening Test and the Minnesota Aphasia Test which could not be meaningfully quantified for statistical analysis.

Measures Obtained from the Indiana
Neuropsychology Battery

Measures 1 through 57 in Appendix A were derived from tests routinely administered to children in the 10 to 14 age range at the Neuropsychology Laboratory of the Indiana University Medical Center. The tests from which these measures were taken included the Wide Range Achievement Test (Jastak, 1946), the Wechsler-Bellevue Intelligence Scale (Wechsler, 1944), Halstead's Neuropsychological Test Battery (Halstead, 1947; Reitan, 1959), the Trail Making Test (Reitan, 1958), a modification of the Halstead-Wepman Aphasia Screening Test (Halstead and Wepman, 1949; Heimburger and Reitan, 1961), a series of tests of sensory and perceptual disturbances (Reitan, 1965), a modification of the Harris Tests of Lateral Dominance (Harris, 1947), and the Peabody Picture Vocabulary Test (Dunn, 1959).

These tests provided a means of comparing Normal Readers and Retarded Readers regarding the probability of lateralized cerebral dysfunction, the configuration of reading and nonreading abilities, and the level of certain specific skills possibly relevant to reading disability. The obvious suitability of the Indiana Neuropsychology Tests for evaluating the relative capabilities of children with reading disability served as a very important factor in the decision to carry out the study reported herein.

Measures Obtained from the
Minnesota Aphasia Test

During the early stages of planning this study Professor Drew pointed out that specific reading disability in the group to be studied might involve the sort of language deficit exhibited by adults classified as aphasic. He suggested that the Minnesota Test for Differential Diagnosis of Aphasia would provide a thorough assessment of this possibility. Dr. Hildred Schuell kindly supplied a copy of the then-current research edition of this test and granted permission for its use.

The Minnesota Aphasia Test, as modified for the present study, yielded 33 quantifiable measures (Measures 58 through 90 in Appendix A). The main modifications were elimination of subtests which essentially duplicated tests in the Indiana battery (e.g., digit span, vocabulary, similarities); elimination of subtests with difficult reading material, since these would only serve to discourage the children with reading disability; and changes in the content of certain items to make them more appropriate for use with school children.

The 33 measures taken from the Minnesota Test included 5 tests of auditory disturbance, 5 tests of visual and reading disturbance, 10 tests of speech and language disturbance, and 13 tests of visual motor and writing disturbance. The joint use of the Minnesota Aphasia Test and the Indiana Neuropsychology Tests provided a broad survey of skills possibly sensitive to cerebral dysfunction, with a particularly detailed evaluation of language skills.

Other Tests

The remaining 19 measures (Measures 91 through 109 in Appendix A) sampled certain abilities of possible relevance that were not explicitly assessed by the Indiana and Minnesota tests. The first 13 of these measures were derived from a test for speed of visual perception and were designed especially for the present study to provide an estimate of relative perceptual speed for printed figures, numbers, letters, nonsense syllables, and words. The remaining 6 measures included tests of reversed figure discrimination, word association, color-form preference, right-left orientation, and visual nonverbal memory.

Classification of Tests According
to Input and Output Requirements

The sheer number of measures obtained in the present study makes it very difficult to prepare a comprehensible account of the scope of testing simply in terms of a list of the abilities presumably sampled by the tests. Nor can the tests be placed in more readily understandable categories on the basis of factorial composition, since the necessary information was lacking for the majority of tests. To provide the reader with a somewhat clearer notion of the range of abilities tested, as many as possible of the measures in Appendix A have been categorized according to input and output requirements. For any given task the input is described in terms of the channel of sensory stimulation and the characteristics of the stimulus presented through the sensory channel. Output requirements are described in terms of the response systems involved in producing the output and the properties of the response product. The resulting classification scheme, although of dubious theoretical ancestry, provides a workable system for describing the variety of skills assessed in the present study.

The categories of input and output are shown in Table 4, with an indication of the number of measures falling into each category and subcategory, and a numerical designation of each measure in each category according to its listing in Appendix A. Of the 21 measures from Appendix A not listed in Table 4, some were composite scores (e.g., Measures 3-7) and others (e.g., Measure 33) involved a complex input.

Input. About half of the measures listed involved visual input; about one fourth had auditory input; and about one fifth involved no sensory input other than initial instructions. Each sensory channel was further subdivided with respect to verbal properties of the stimulus. About one third of the visual tasks involved verbal stimuli, and could thus be considered to sample some aspect of reading. The remaining two thirds of nonverbal visual tasks largely involved geometric figures or pictures.

All but one of the 20 measures with auditory input were verbal; the lone instance of nonverbal auditory input occurring on the Seashore Rhythm Test (Measure 27).

Of the 11 tests with somesthetic* input, only 2 measures requiring identification of numbers written on the fingertips were verbal.

The 16 measures classified as having no input involved the execution of a response on the basis of a simple instruction such as "Write your name as fast as you can," and with no further input requirement.

Output. The output of each task was classified as verbal or nonverbal. There were some tasks with a verbal input and nonverbal output, some with a nonverbal input and verbal output, and others with entirely verbal or entirely nonverbal input and output requirements. Verbal output could take the form of speech or writing, and nonverbal output could occur in the form of drawing, manual manipulation, or a multiple choice or pointing response.

---

*The term *somesthetic* is used herein to refer to sensory input on tasks where the subject was required to respond on the basis of touch or spatial position or a combination of these tactual and kinesthetic stimuli, and in the absence of any visual and auditory cues.

TABLE 4

Input and output requirements of 88 of the measures obtained in this study. The number of measures in each category and subcategory is indicated, as is the numerical designation of each measure (Appendix A).

INPUT		OUTPUT			MEASURE NO.
VISUAL 41	Verbal 14	VERBAL: 4	Speech	2	(1,67)
			Writing	2	(83,89)
		NONVERBAL: 10	Manual	9	(91,95,96,97,99,100, 101,102,103)
			Choice	1	(66)
	Nonverbal 27	VERBAL: 5	Speech	3	(15,72,75)
			Writing	2	(86,90)
		NONVERBAL: 22	Drawing	6	(36,37,38,39,78,81)
			Manual	8	(14,16,17,31,92,93, 94,98)
			Choice	8	(21,43,44,63,105,107, 108,109)
AUDITORY 20	Verbal 19	VERBAL: 19	Speech	16	(8,9,10,11,12,13,60, 62,68,69,71,73,76,77, 87,106)
			Writing	3	(2,85,88)
		NONVERBAL:		0	
	Nonverbal 1	VERBAL:		0	
		NONVERBAL:	Choice	1	(27)
SOMES- THETIC 11	Verbal 2	VERBAL:	Speech	2	(47,48)
		NONVERBAL:		0	
	Nonverbal 9	VERBAL:	Speech	2	(49,50)
		NONVERBAL: 7	Manual	3	(22,23,24)
			Choice	4	(41,42,45,46)
NO INPUT 16		VERBAL: 5	Speech	2	(70,74)
			Writing	3	(56,57,84)
		NONVERBAL: 11	Drawing	3	(25,79,80)
			Manual	6	(26,29,30,32,54,55)
			Choice	2	(51,53)

Output measures were not distributed evenly across the input categories. The types of task involved in the various input-output categories can best be illustrated by specific examples. The topmost category in Table 4 includes tasks with visual verbal input and verbal speech output. Such tasks require oral reading, and 1 of the 2 tasks in this category served as the criterion of reading achievement. The assessment of speed of visual perception involved tasks with both visual verbal and visual nonverbal input and nonverbal manual output.

A number of copying tasks are examples of entirely nonverbal tasks, with visual nonverbal input and nonverbal drawing output. The majority of auditory tasks were entirely verbal, and can be classified as question-and-answer problems with auditory verbal input and verbal speech output. The majority of somesthetic tasks, on the other hand, were entirely nonverbal and required either a manual or a choice response.

Summary of input-output requirements. The primary defining characteristic of specific reading disability in the present study was oral reading retardation, a task involving visual verbal input and spoken verbal output. The measures used in this study covered a wide range of input and output requirements and were intended to provide a systematic description of the extent of nonreading deficit. If reading disability were truly specific, the Retarded Readers should differ from Normal Readers only on tasks involving visual verbal input.

The most noticeable imbalance of test coverage revealed by the survey of input-output requirements occurred in tests with auditory input, where there was a scarcity of tasks with nonverbal content. Since auditory verbal tasks should be most closely related to reading deficit, the lack of auditory nonverbal tasks was not considered to be of crucial significance. However, it should be noted that this deficiency in the test battery might not have been recognized if the tests had not been classified according to input-output requirements.

The distribution of input-output requirements can also be examined in relation to the range of abilities covered by standard batteries of aptitude tests. Much more emphasis was placed on the evaluation of basic perceptual and motor skills in the present study, and there were relatively fewer tests of complex skills such as inductive reasoning. Should analysis of the more basic skills prove of little or no value in describing the pattern of disability associated with specific reading disability, an investigation of more complex skills might be indicated for future studies.

Tests which Permitted Inferences about
Lateralized Cerebral Deficit

Certain configurations of the tests within the Indiana Neuro-psychology Battery are predictive of lateralized cerebral deficit in adults (Reitan, 1959). Inferences regarding lateralization are based on 2 independent kinds of evidence: a marked discrepancy between verbal and nonverbal abilities, and a pronounced deficiency in the functioning of one side of the body relative to the other. The difference between Verbal IQ (Measure 4) and Performance IQ (Measure 5) on the Wechsler-Bellevue Scale is indicative of the verbal-nonverbal discrepancy, while differences in proficiency with the right hand or the left hand are often demonstrated on the Halstead Tapping Test (Measures 29 and 30) and the Halstead Tactual Performance Test (Measures 22 and 23). Supporting evidence may be obtained from other tests with specific verbal and nonverbal requirements, and from other tests of sensory, motor, and perceptual functioning on which the 2 sides of the body are separately assessed. Many of the subtests of the Minnesota Aphasia Test also provide information regarding the relative status of verbal and nonverbal abilities.

If specific reading disability were a result of lateralized cerebral dysfunction, and if the behavioral manifestations in children were comparable to those seen in adults, then the Retarded Readers should tend to have a relatively low Verbal IQ and a relative weakness of functioning of the right side of the body in comparison with Normal Readers. For "truly" left-handed subjects, of course, the left cerebral hemisphere would not necessarily subserve verbal abilities, and thus the right side of the body would not necessarily be the deficient side.

Inferences regarding the presence or absence of nonlateralized cerebral dysfunction in Retarded Readers would be more difficult. An important consideration in making such inferences in adults is the relationship between the overall level of tested ability and the educational level of the patient. Such a criterion would be irrelevant in the present study. In the absence of any independent criterion of the integrity of brain function, all inferences regarding nonlateralized cerebral deficit should be recognized as hypothetical.

Tests which Permitted Evaluation of Other Theories of Reading Disability

The test of right-left orientation (Measure 104) provided a means of assessing Hermann's (1959) hypothesis that directional confusion is the fundamental disorder in reading disability. This hypothesis would be supported by a finding that the Retarded Readers were as severely deficient in right-left orientation as they were in reading achievement.

Certain aspects of Orton's theory (1937) could also be evaluated. The lateral dominance examination (Measures 51-57) provided an indication of inconsistencies in hand, eye, and foot preference among Retarded Readers. It should be noted at the outset that the incidence of nominal left handedness fell within the range of normal expectations for all groups, with 5 of the 39 Retarded Readers, 7 of the 39 Male Normal Readers, and 4 of the 39 Female Normal Readers being left handed. Since handedness was not a criterion of selection for this study, it can be concluded immediately that the population of Retarded Readers from which the subjects of the present study were drawn did not contain an unusually high incidence of left handedness. Other aspects of strephosymbolia, as postulated by Orton, could not be tested. However, tests such as the Thurstone Reversals Test (Measure 105) did provide indirect indication of some of the possible manifestations of incomplete dominance.

Some of the other proposed explanations of reading disability such as those of de Hirsch (1954) and Birch (1962) could best be evaluated by overall inspection of the test results of the present study. The syndromes of nonreading deficit described by other investigators such as Myklebust and Johnson (1962), Rabinovitch et al. (1954), and Silver and Hagin (1960) can be evaluated by direct comparison with whatever patterning of nonreading deficiencies is found in the present study. Explanations of specific reading disability in terms of hereditary factors and in terms of prenatal and perinatal disorders can be evaluated with reference to case history information, as described below.

CASE HISTORY

Information regarding birth and development of the child and the incidence of reading problems in the child's family was obtained by an interview with one of the child's parents, usually the mother. During this interview the two forms shown in Appendix B (p.165) were completed. The Birth and Developmental History form included specific sets of questions regarding pregnancy and delivery, early development, illnesses and accidents, education, status of siblings, family handedness, and present status of child, and concluded with a judgment of the reliability of the informant. This form was modeled after case history forms used in other investigations of childhood disorders. The form for family history of reading problems, devised especially for this study, included sets of questions regarding the reading history of the mother, the father, the siblings, the grandparents, and other relatives, and concluded with detailed questions regarding the child's own reading history.

The case history information will be described and evaluated in a later chapter. It should be noted here, however, that although all of the parents interviewed were trustworthy informants, their recall of the details of developmental history and family history was often admittedly faulty. The case history information of this study, then, cannot be considered comparable in validity to information obtained by means of longitudinal investigations or information retrospectively obtained from hospital and clinic records.

NEUROLOGICAL EXAMINATION

Each of the Retarded Readers was given a neurological examination by a Resident Neurologist of the Indiana University Neurology Department. Over half of the Normal Readers were also examined in order to establish that no gross neurological abnormalities would be disclosed in the examination of children who were making normal educational progress.

The examination procedure, as planned by Professor Drew, was appropriate for the evaluation of children with relatively mild and subtle deficits ("soft signs"), and included an overall evaluation of sensory, motor, and reflex functioning, directional orientation, and other standard neurological procedures. Although an electroencephalographic (EEG) examination of brain activity might have been relevant (cf., Muehl, Knott, and Benton, 1965), permission for this type of examination could not be obtained from school officials.

CHAPTER FOUR

Procedure, Scoring, and
Methods of Analysis

PROCEDURE

Administration of Tests

The Retarded Readers were tested at the Indiana University Medical Center. The Neuropsychology Tests were given in 2 sessions on one day or in 3 sessions over 2 different days at the Neuropsychology Laboratory. The remaining tests, including the Minnesota Aphasia Test, were given in a separate session at the Institute of Psychiatric Research.

The Normal Readers were tested in a trailer located outside the Fall Creek Heights Elementary School. The trailer was completely equipped as a testing laboratory, with heating and air-conditioning facilities. Test materials were exactly the same as those used for Retarded Readers. The tests were usually given in 3 sessions over 2 different days.

The tests were administered by technicians who had been carefully trained to give each test in a standard manner. Insofar as possible, the tests were always given in the same order and under the same set of conditions. This standardization of testing techniques was intended to reduce errors of measurement and to minimize the influence of any possible examiner bias.

None of the children in the present study gave any indication of failure to understand instructions, and all appeared sufficiently well-motivated throughout the testing. If anything, the testing conditions for Normal Readers were somewhat less favorable, since the testing space in the trailer was slightly smaller and there tended to be more outside distraction from playground noise.

Neurological Examination

The neurological examination required 15 to 30 minutes. The Retarded Readers were examined on a day when they came to the Neuropsychology Laboratory for testing. The Normal Readers were examined in the testing trailer during several visits by Dr. Cruz. With this type of examination, and where the status of the patient is known, the influence of examiner bias cannot be evaluated.

Case History

Case history information was obtained from the parents of Retarded Readers on one of the days the child was brought in for testing.

Since the Normal Readers were tested at school during the school day, special arrangements were made for interviewing the parents of these children in their own home.

SCORING

The method of scoring each of the quantified measures is indicated in Appendix A (p.151). Wherever an objective scoring method was already available, this procedure was used. In certain instances, several different tests of the same type of ability were combined in order to increase the dispersion of scores. This was done for hand and foot preference (Measures 51 and 53), for the measures of articulation on the Minnesota Aphasia Test (Measure 68), and for the measures of spatial orientation (Measure 104). Several composite scores were recorded. These included Full Scale IQ, Verbal IQ, and Performance IQ, and Verbal and Performance Weighted Scores on the Wechsler-Bellevue Scale (Measures 3-7), and total drawing scores for drawings on the Halstead-Wepman and the Minnesota Aphasia tests (Measures 40 and 82). The score for oral presentation of the Peabody Picture Vocabulary Test was expressed in terms of both total correct (Measure 33) and oral IQ (Measure 34). For almost all measures it is obvious whether a "good" score is high or low because most tests were scored in terms of either errors or correct responses.

No precise scoring rules were available for any of the drawings on the Halstead-Wepman and Minnesota Aphasis Tests except for the drawing of a man (Measure 80), which was scored according to rules formulated by Goodenough (1926). For the remaining drawings (Measure 36-39, 78, 79, and 81), quantified scoring rules were devised according to the same general rationale as that used by Goodenough for the drawing of a man. Since the scoring of drawings required subjective judgments, the drawings were scored in random order and identified only by a code number. All drawings were independently scored by 2 different individuals, with the final score being an average of the 2 scores.

A number of items from the Halstead-Wepman and the Minnesota Aphasia Tests could not be quantified for statistical analysis because of the relatively small number of scoring categories, or because the tasks were so easy that almost all performances were errorless. These are given in Appendix A as unnumbered measures.

Quantification of the results of the neurological examination and the case history information consisted of simple counts of frequency of occurrence of symptoms and etiological events. The methods used to evaluate these results are described below.

STATISTICAL ANALYSIS

The test results were analyzed by several different statistical procedures: a test-by-test comparison of the average performance of Normal and Retarded Readers by analysis of covariance; examination of the interrelationships among reading and other abilities for each group separately by factor analysis; an estimation of which nonreading measures best discriminate between Normal and Retarded Readers by means of a stepwise regression procedure; and calculation of the optimal weighted scores for differentiating Normal and Retarded Readers by discriminant analysis of several sets of nonreading measures. All computations were carried out at the Indiana University Research Computing Center with an IBM 701 Computer, using programs from the BIMD Computer Programs Manual (1961).

Analysis of Covariance (BIMD 20)

Analysis of covariance was used to test the significance of the difference between the mean scores of Normal and Retarded Readers on each of the 109 measures listed in Appendix A. This statistic assumes that the scores for a given measure are normally distributed within each group and that the groups do not differ in variability. Certain measures were not normally distributed in one or both groups because of a high proportion of perfect or near-perfect scores or because of a restriction in the range of possible scores. Such nonnormal distributions will be noted in the discussion of results. The analysis of covariance technique permitted an increase in the sensitivity of the statistical tests of the difference between groups by removing variability of test performance attributable to age. This reduced the possibility that an improvement of ability as a function of increasing age within each group would introduce enough variability to mask any systematic difference between groups. Separate analyses were made for differences between Retarded Readers and Male Normal Readers, Retarded Readers and Female Normal Readers, and Male Normal Readers and Female Normal Readers. In addition, separate computations were made for groups from which left-handed subjects had been excluded. The only analysis to be presented in detail is the comparison between the entire groups of Retarded Readers and Male Normal Readers. These results are described in Chapter 5.

Factor Analysis (BIMD 17)

Factor analysis provided a means of determining the interrelatedness of reading and nonreading measures within each group, and also a comparison of the factorial structures of the abilities of Retarded Readers and Normal Readers. Since the computer program could not accommodate all of the quantified measures, a set of 79 measures was selected for factor analysis. The factor analysis of these measures was performed for the entire groups of Retarded Readers and Male Normal Readers. The results of these analyses are described in Chapter 8.

Generalized Stepwise Regression (BIMD 34)

A multiple-correlational procedure designated as Generalized Stepwise Regression provided some insight into the types of nonreading

measures which best differentiated Male Normal Readers from Retarded Readers. A set of 57 measures that did not require reading
ability were selected for this analysis. The analysis was carried out
in a series of steps, with an additional measure added at each step.
The measure added at each step was the one which produced the
greatest increase of the multiple correlation with reading status. The
relevance of this statistic will be more obvious when the actual results
of the stepwise regression analysis are discussed in Chapter 9.

Systematic Discriminant Analysis (BIMD 05 and BIMD 04M)

Another multiple regression procedure, discriminant analysis, was
used to provide more information regarding the measures of nonreading ability which differentiated the Retarded Readers from the Normal
Readers. The stepwise regression procedure was continued until 29
measures had been selected. Then a discriminant analysis was performed for 14 sets of measures which included the variables selected
at a number of different stages of the stepwise regression. By means
of this discriminant analysis, differential weights were computed for
the component measures of each set to produce a total score that would
best differentiate between Male Normal Readers and Retarded Readers.
This provided a slightly different means of exploring the pattern of
nonreading deficit in Retarded Readers. This procedure will also be
clarified by discussion in relation to the actual findings of the study in
Chapter 9.

Arbitrary Discriminant Analysis (BIMD 05)

The final direct statistical comparison of the test performance of
Normal and Retarded Readers involved the method of discriminant
analysis described above, but with different sets of nonreading measures. Several sets of nonreading measures were arbitrarily selected
to investigate their practical value for predicting reading status. From
a set of 18 nonreading measures, 10 different subsets of measures
ranging in size from 2 to 18 measures were selected to determine the
accuracy of prediction provided by sets containing tests of general
nonreading abilities, verbal abilities, nonverbal abilities, easily administered tests, visual abilities, motor abilities, complex visual and
auditory discriminations, visual and auditory short term memory,
relatively simple visual and auditory skills, relatively simple visual,
auditory, and motor skills, and simple stored information. These results are presented in Chapter 9.

EVALUATION OF NEUROLOGICAL STATUS

Neurological status was evaluated by a neurologist (A. L. Drew) on
the basis of the report of the neurological examination and the case

history information. A judgment of neurological status based upon the neurological examination alone was made on a six-point scale ranging from "normal" to "definitely pathological" for each of the 39 Retarded Readers, 22 Male Normal Readers, and 21 Female Normal Readers. The neurological reports were examined in random order with no identifying information. A further judgment of neurological status was based upon joint evaluation of the neurological report and the case history information. The same six-point judgmental scale was used, and once again the case material was randomized and anonymous. These judgments, which are discussed in Chapter 6, provided a means of assessing the incidence of significant neurological deficit among Retarded Readers.

NEUROPSYCHOLOGICAL INTERPRETATION OF TEST PATTERNS

Reitan and his associates at the Indiana University Neuropsychology Laboratory have developed procedures for predicting the location, extent, and type of cerebral lesions in individual patients (Reitan, 1959; 1965). These predictions are based upon an examination of the results of the Neuropsychology Test Battery, plus knowledge of the patient's age, education, and handedness, but with no additional information regarding case history or present neurological status and no personal contact with the patient. A modification of this predictive procedure provided another type of inference regarding the neurological and neuropsychological status of the Retarded Readers in the present study.

Individual judgments of the probability of cerebral deficit for each of the Retarded Readers and each of the Male Normal Readers were made independently by 2 highly experienced neuropsychologists (R. M. Reitan and H. Kløve). Their estimates of possible lateralization and severity of cerebral dysfunction were based upon examination of test results from which all tests requiring reading had been eliminated. The test results of Normal and Retarded Readers were examined in random order, with no identifying information regarding reading status. The results of this analysis are presented in Chapter 7.

ANALYSIS OF INDIVIDUAL TEST PROFILES OF RETARDED READERS

The final type of analysis involved examination of the profiles of test scores for selected individuals in the Retarded Reader group. These profiles were expressed in terms of percentiles of the Normal Readers' distribution for each measure. This form of individual analysis was employed to assess the likelihood that reading retardation, as defined in this study, can be associated with a number of different patterns of nonreading deficit, such as visual perceptual difficulty, impairment of auditory verbal processing, or generalized language difficulty. The results of this analysis are presented in Chapter 10.

CHAPTER FIVE

Test-by-Test Comparison of Normal Readers and Retarded Readers

Statistical comparisons of Retarded Readers and Normal Readers on individual tests are presented in this chapter. These analyses were carried out for 103 of the 109 measures listed in Appendix A (p. 151). The comparisons of the groups of 39 Retarded Readers and 39 Male Normal Readers are described in detail. At the end of this chapter, relatively brief mention is made of the comparisons of Retarded Readers and Female Normal Readers and the comparisons of Retarded Readers and Male Normal Readers with left-handed subjects excluded. These additional analyses did not alter the general trends observed in comparisons of the entire groups of Retarded Readers and Male Normal Readers.

The overall magnitude of observed deficit in Retarded Readers will be considered first, followed by examination of the results for tests of reading and directly related skills, verbal and nonverbal IQ measures, measures classified according to input-output characteristics, tests indicative of cerebral dysfunction, aphasia tests, and tests relevant to previous theories of reading disability. The test-by-test comparison of Retarded and Normal Readers is of fundamental importance because the configuration of nonreading deficit in Retarded Readers should be most clearly revealed by this analysis. The remaining statistical analyses of test scores, to be presented in Chapters 8 and 9, serve primarily to indicate interrelationships among measures associated with reading deficit.

Before the results of the test-by-test comparisons are described, the procedure of statistical analysis and the rationale for interpretation of statistically significant differences between groups will be discussed.

STATISTICAL METHOD

The technique of analysis of covariance provided a statistical comparison of the average scores of Retarded Readers and Normal Readers for 103 of the 109 measures listed in Appendix A. Near-errorless performance by both groups precluded a meaningful analysis of the remaining 6 measures (Measures 59, 61, 71, 72, 83, and 84). Analysis of covariance was chosen as the statistical test for comparing the 2 groups because the sensitivity of comparison could be increased by elimination of variability attributable to age.

The results of analysis of covariance for the groups of 39 Retarded Readers and 39 Male Normal Readers are summarized in Appendix C (p. 169), where the following information is given for each measure: the unadjusted mean and the standard deviation of test scores for each group, an indication of the form of the distribution of scores, the statistical ratio (F') obtained by analysis of covariance, the level of statistical significance denoted by this ratio, and the direction of group superiority.

Group Means

The group means given in Appendix C are averages of original scores. The analysis of covariance is actually based upon a comparison of age-adjusted means (Walker and Lev, 1953). However, the 2 groups were so similar in average age that the adjustments were negligible, and it was felt that the unadjusted means would be more informative.

Standard Deviations and Distribution Characteristics

For a parametric statistic such as analysis of covariance, the comparison of group differences is valid only when certain requirements regarding the distribution of scores within groups are met. Within each group the scores must be dispersed around the mean in a manner that conforms reasonably well to a normal distribution; and the amount of variability, as indicated by the standard deviation, must be of the same order of magnitude for both groups.

Abnormalities in the distributions of scores in the present study tended to occur in one of 2 forms. When a test was too easy, the dispersion of scores was restricted by a high proportion of perfect or near-perfect scores; and when only a few scoring categories were available the spread of scores was sharply restricted. Restricted distributions are indicated under the column heading "Dist." in Appendix C. For the majority of measures the distributions were adequately dispersed.

The occurrence of a non-normal distribution does not necessarily render the statistical analysis meaningless. It simply indicates that the statistical result must be interpreted with explicit reference to the observed abnormality of distribution. Restricted distributions, whether imposed by a large number of perfect scores or by too few scoring categories, could result in a statistical ratio which underestimates the magnitude of difference between groups. In such a case a statistically significant difference could be accepted as indicating a reliable difference between groups for that measure. If anything, the proportion of measures showing statistically significant differences between groups was probably reduced by inclusion of measures with restricted distributions.

The requirement that the variability of scores should be of the same order of magnitude for each group can be assessed by inspection of the standard deviations for each group on each measure, as listed under the "SD" column in Appendix C. It can be seen that the standard deviations of the 2 groups were quite comparable for most measures, with the main exceptions involving distributions which were non-normal for one or both groups.

F' Ratio and Level of Statistical Significance

In general, the larger the F' ratio the more reliable is the difference between group means. Where analysis of covariance is carried out for 2 groups of 39 subjects each, an F' ratio of 3.97 or greater is significant beyond the .05 level, an F' ratio of 6.99 or greater is significant beyond the .01 level, and an F' ratio of 11.75 or greater is significant beyond the .001 level. Statistical significance beyond the .05 level indicates that a given difference between means would occur by chance fewer than 5 times in 100 comparisons of randomly selected groups; statistical significance beyond the .01 level indicates chance occurrence of a given mean difference less than 1 time in 100 comparisons of random samples; and significance beyond the .001 level indicates chance occurrence less than 1 time in 1,000. These significance levels are applicable when the distributions of scores meet the requirements of the statistical test, as discussed above.

Direction of Superiority in Statistically Significant Differences

On all tests that were scored in terms of response rate, number of correct responses, or number of errors, a group's superiority was demonstrated by higher response rate, more correct responses, or fewer errors. On such tests a significant difference clearly indicates that one of the groups was superior to the other for that particular skill. Almost all of the tests yielded this type of score, with the only real exceptions being the measures of hand, eye, and foot dominance (Measures 51, 52, and 53). For these measures, consistency of dominance can be considered superior (Harris, 1957). In the last column of Appendix C are listed the direction of statistically significant differences, with "N" designating measures on which Normal Readers were superior and "R" designating measures on which Retarded Readers were superior.

RATIONALE FOR INTERPRETATION
OF SIGNIFICANT DIFFERENCES

The differentiation of groups in reading achievement and the matching of groups in Performance IQ, along with the other selection procedures described in Chapter 3, were integral parts of the plan for investigating the structure of abilities of children with specific reading disability. The reading criterion defined the reading problem, and the nonverbal intelligence criterion defined the specificity of the problem. The statistical comparison of the 2 groups on the remaining quantitative measures should demonstrate the extent and the configuration of additional disability in the Retarded Readers.

Restrictions Imposed by the Reading Criterion

The main criterion of differentiation was retardation of no fewer than 2 years for Retarded Readers and no more than one year for Normal Readers on Measure 1, Oral Reading Achievement (see Table 2 on page 22 for the distributions of reading achievement scores). Since a very large difference between groups was purposely introduced by this criterion, the statistical magnitude of the difference between groups should be very large for the reading achievement measure relative to non-criterion measures. The group difference imposed by the reading criterion should also operate in a direct and obvious manner to produce differences between groups on other measures requiring reading.

Restrictions Imposed by Matching the Groups in Nonverbal Intelligence

In contrast to the differentiation of groups by the reading criterion, the groups were equated in Performance IQ to satisfy this aspect of the definition of specific reading disability (see Table 3 on page 23 for distributions of Performance IQ). The matching of groups in Performance IQ (Measure 5) not only precluded a significant difference between groups for this measure, but directly reduced the possibility of a significant difference between groups for any of the 5 component subtests of the Performance Scale (Measures 14-18). It is also reasonable to assume that the matching of groups in Performance IQ would tend to produce a similarity between groups in any nonverbal skill highly correlated with Performance IQ.

OVERALL MAGNITUDE OF DIFFERENCES
BETWEEN GROUPS

Analysis of covariance was performed for 103 measures. The Normal Readers obtained significantly superior scores on 62 of these measures, the Retarded Readers were significantly superior on 5 measures, and the groups did not differ significantly on 36 measures. The results for each measure are given in Appendix C, where the original order of measures has been preserved.

The results are presented in somewhat different form in Tables 5, 6, and 7. In Table 5 the measures on which Normal Readers were

TABLE 5

Tests on which Normal Readers were significantly superior to Retarded Readers, ranked according to size of the F′ Ratio, with composite and duplicate measures excluded. Input-output characteristics and reading requirements are indicated (v = visual, a = auditory, s = somesthetic, V = verbal, N = nonverbal, s = speech, w = writing, m = manual, d = drawing, c = choice, R = tests requiring skills directly related to reading).

RANK	MEASURE	INPUT – OUTPUT	F′
Significant Beyond the .001 Level			
1	1. Oral reading *(Reading Criterion)*	vV–Vs–R	325
2	2. Written spelling	aV–Vw–R	261
3	87. Oral spelling, Minnesota Aphasia	aV–Vs–R	243
4	88. Writing sentences to dictation, Minn. Aphasia	aV–Vw–R	198*
5	35. Peabody Vocabulary, written words	vVN–Nc–R	119
6	73. Word rhyming, Minnesota Aphasia	aV–Vs	107*
7	8. W–B Information subtest	aV–Vs	99
8	86. Writing words, picture stimulus, Minn. Aphasia	aV–Vw–R	86*
9	100. Visual perceptual speed, nonsense syllables	vV–Nm–R	74
10	90. Writing paragraph, picture stimulus, Minn. Aphasia	vV–Vw–R	68
11	11. W–B Arithmetic subtest	aV–Vs	57
12	28. Halstead Speech Perception Test	avV–Nc–R	56
13	12. W–B Similarities subtest	aV–Vs	52
14	89. Written sentences, Minnesota Aphasia	vV–Vw–R	51*
15	101. Visual perceptual speed, words	vV–Nm–R	49
16	70. Serial responses, Minnesota Aphasia	– – –Vs	46*
17	13. W–B Vocabulary subtest	aV–Vs	46
18	102. Visual perceptual speed, unspaced words	vV–Nm–R	43
19	67. Oral reading sentences, Minnesota Aphasia	vV–Vs–R	33*
20	105. Reversed figure discrimination, Thurstone	vN–Nc	26*
21	27. Halstead Rhythm Test	aN–Nc	25*
22	93. Visual perceptual speed, nonsense letters	vN–Nm	24
23	19. Trail Making, numbers, Part A	vVN–Nm–R	21
24	109. Visual temporal memory for figures	vN–Nc	21
25	80. Draw a man, Minnesota Aphasia	– – –Nd	21
26	108. Visual spatial memory for figures	vN–Nc	20
27	92. Visual perceptual speed, geometric figures	vN–Nm	19
28	68. Articulation, Minnesota Aphasia	aV–Vs	18*
29	33. Peabody Vocabulary, oral words	avVN–Nc	18
30	99. Visual perceptual speed, nonsense syllables	vV–Nm–R	17
31	66. Written sentence comprehension, Minn. Aphasia	vV–Nc–R	16*
32	78. Copy complex figure, Minnesota Aphasia	vN–Nd	16
33	96. Visual perceptual speed, letters in syllables	vV–Nm–R	16
34	64. Match words to pictures, Minnesota Aphasia	vV–Nc–R	16*
35	18. W–B Digit Symbol (Performance subtest)	vVN–Nd–R	14
36	20. Trail Making, numbers & letters, Part B	vVN–Nm–R	14
37	77. Retelling paragraph, Minnesota Aphasia	aV–Vs	13
38	60. Repeat spoken sentences, Minnesota Aphasia	aV–Vs	13
39	95. Visual perceptual speed, letters	vV–Nm–R	13

*Restricted distribution of scores in one or both groups.

TABLE 5 (continued)

Tests on which Normal Readers were significantly superior to Retarded Readers, ranked according to size of the F' ratio.

RANK	MEASURE	INPUT – OUTPUT	F'
Significant Beyond the .01 Level			
40	9. W-B Comprehension subtest	aV-Vs	11
41	10. W-B Digit Span subtest	aV-Vs	10
42	91. Visual perceptual speed, numbers	vV-Nm-R	10
43	21. Halstead Category Test	vN-Nc	10
44	98. Visual perceptual speed, sequential forms	vN-Nm	9
45	103. Visual perceptual speed, numbers	vV-Nm-R	9
46	94. Visual perceptual speed, Gestalt figures	vN-Nm	8
47	54. Strength of grip, preferred hand	---Nm	7
Significant Beyond the .05 Level			
48	31. Halstead Time Sense Test, visual	vN-Nm	6.5
49	76. Spoken sentence formulation, Minnesota Aphasia	aV-Vs	6.5*
50	46. Finger agnosia, left hand	sN-Nc	6.4*
51	62. Comprehension of spoken paragraph, Minn. Aphasia	aV-Vs	5.6*
52	85. Writing letters to dictation, Minnesota Aphasia	aV-Vw-R	5.5*
53	65. Matching printed to spoken words, Minn. Aphasia	avV-Nc-R	5.0*
54	58. Visual symbol recognition, Minnesota Aphasia	avV-Nc-R	4.8*
55	55. Strength of grip, nonpreferred hand	---Nm	4.5
56	104. Spatial orientation	avVN-Nm	4.4*
57	37. Copy cross, Halstead-Wepman Test	vN-Nd	4.2

*Restricted distribution of scores in one or both groups.

significantly superior are ranked according to the magnitude of the F' ratio, with composite and duplicate measures (Measures 3, 4, 6, 34, 82) excluded. The F' ratio and the input-output characteristics of each measure are given. For convenience in the interpretation of tabular data, tests which appeared to involve skills directly related to reading are indicated, as are tests with non-normal distributions of scores for one or both groups. The classification of tests as reading-related was, in a number of instances, quite arbitrary.

For the 57 measures ranked in this manner, the difference between groups was significant beyond the .001 level for 39 measures, significant beyond the .01 level for an additional 8 measures, and significant beyond the .05 level for the remaining 10 measures. As noted in the table, 26 of these 57 measures involved skills directly related to reading, and one of the measures was a component of the nonverbal intelligence criterion.

The 5 measures on which Retarded Readers were significantly superior to Normal Readers are listed in Table 6. Only one measure involved a difference significant beyond the .001 level, another was significant beyond the .01 level, and the remaining 3 comparisons were significant beyond the .05 level. All but one of these measures involved somesthetic nonverbal input, the exception being a component subtest of the nonverbal intelligence criterion.

TABLE 6

Tests on which Retarded Readers were significantly superior to Normal Readers, ranked according to size of the F' Ratio, with composite and duplicate measures excluded. Input-output characteristics are indicated (v = visual, s = somesthetic, V = verbal, N = nonverbal, m = manual, s = speech).

RANK	MEASURE	INPUT–OUTPUT	F'
Significant Beyond the .001 Level			
1	22. Halstead Tactual Performance, pref. hand	sN–nM	16
Significant Beyond the .01 Level			
2	17. W.B. Object assembly (Performance subtest)	vN–Nm	10
Significant Beyond the .05 Level			
3	49. Tactile form recognition, right hand	sN–Vs	6.4
4	50. Tactile form recognition, left hand	sN–Vs	4.4
5	24. Halstead Tactual Performance, both hands	sN–Nm	4.2

Table 7 lists 39 measures on which the groups did not differ significantly, including the 6 measures on which both groups performed so nearly perfectly that no statistical test was necessary (Measures 59, 61, 71, 72, 83, and 84) and excluding 3 composite measures (Measures 5, 7, and 40). A preponderance of measures with nonverbal input-output characteristics may be noted, including 3 of the component subtests of the nonverbal intelligence criterion. The list also includes 4 measures of skills directly related to reading, all of which involved non-normal distributions.

It is immediately apparent from even a casual inspection of Appendix C, and Tables 5, 6, and 7, that the disability of Retarded Readers was not restricted to reading or skills directly related to reading, but extended to a relatively large number of nonreading skills. Among the nonreading measures on which Retarded Readers were deficient were a great many tasks with either auditory verbal or visual nonverbal input. Many of the measures on which Retarded Readers did not differ from Normal Readers were nonverbal in both input and output requirements. And all but one of the few tasks on which Retarded Readers were superior involved input through the body senses rather than vision and hearing. The general implications of these findings will be considered after a detailed examination of the results.

ABILITIES DIRECTLY RELATED TO READING

As expected, the difference between groups of greatest statistical magnitude, an F' ratio of 325, occurred for Measure 1, the criterion of reading achievement. This difference was, of course, purposely imposed by the selection of groups. The next largest magnitudes of

TABLE 7

Tests on which Retarded Readers and Normal Readers were not significantly different, with composite and duplicate measures excluded. Input-output characteristics (v = visual, a = auditory, s = somesthetic, V = verbal, N = nonverbal, s = speech, m = manual, c = choice, R = tests requiring skills directly related to reading) and distribution characteristics (R = restricted distribution in one or both groups) are indicated.

MEASURE	INPUT–OUTPUT	DISTRI-BUTION
14. W–B Picture Arrangement (<u>Performance subtest</u>)	vN-Nm	
15. W–B Picture Completion (<u>Performance subtest</u>)	vN-Nm	
16. W–B Block design (<u>Performance subtest</u>)	vN-Nm	
23. Halstead Tactual Performance, nonpref. hand	sN-Nm	
25. Halstead Tactual Performance, memory	---Nd	
26. Halstead Tactual Performance, location	---Nm	
29. Halstead Tapping Speed, preferred hand	---Nm	
30. Halstead Tapping Speed, nonpreferred hand	---Nm	
32. Halstead Time Sense Test, memory	---Nm	
36. Copy square, Halstead-Wepman Test	vN-Nd	
38. Copy triangle, Halstead-Wepman Test	vN-Nd	
39. Copy key, Halstead-Wepman Test	vN-Nd	
41. Tactile suppression, right hand	sN-Nc	R
42. Tactile suppression, left hand	sN-Nc	R
43. Visual suppression, right field	vN-Nc	R
44. Visual suppression, left field	vN-Nc	R
45. Finger agnosia, right hand	sN-Nc	R
47. Finger tip number writing, right hand	sV-Vs-R	R
48. Finger tip number writing, left hand	sV-Vs-R	R
51. Lateral dominance, hand preference	---Nc	R
52. Lateral dominance, eye preference	vN-Nc	R
53. Lateral dominance, foot preference	---Nc	R
56. Writing speed, preferred hand	---Vw	
57. Writing speed, nonpreferred hand	---Vw	
59. Retention span, items named serially, Minn. Aphasia	avV-Nc	R*
61. Following directions, Minnesota Aphasia	avV-Nm	R*
63. Matching forms, Minnesota Aphasia	vN-Nc	R
69. Sentence completion, Minnesota Aphasia	aV-Vs	R
71. Response to questions, Minnesota Aphasia	aV-Vs	R*
72. Naming pictures, Minnesota Aphasia	vN-Vs	R*
74. Expressing ideas, Minnesota Aphasia	---Vs	
75. Picture description, Minnesota Aphasia	vN-Vs	
79. Draw a house, Minnesota Aphasia	---Nd	
81. Reproduce wheel, Schuell Test	vN-Nd	
83. Reproduce letters, Minnesota Aphasia	vV-Vw-R	R*
84. Write numerals, Minnesota Aphasia	---Vw-R	R*
97. Visual perceptual speed, two letters	vV-Nm-R	
106. Word association	aV-Vs	
107. Color-form preference	vN-Nc	

*No statistical test because of the high proportion of perfect performances in both groups.

difference were in written spelling achievement (Measure 2) and oral spelling (Measure 87). Thus, the Retarded Readers tended to be as poor in spelling as they were in reading, and this included oral spelling, which had no visual input component.

The Retarded Readers were also significantly impaired on the other 10 measures for which reading or spelling was essential. For 9 of these, including measures of a number of different types of reading and spelling skill, the difference was significant beyond the .001 level (Measures 28, 35, 64, 66, 67, 86, 88, 89, and 90). The remaining task (Measure 65) was a very simple word recognition task designed for adult aphasic patients, and it proved to be so simple even for the Retarded Readers that the groups were only differentiated at the .05 level. The results for reading and spelling tasks demonstrate that the Retarded Readers were deficient in all aspects of reading and spelling. It is unlikely that a more thorough survey of reading and spelling skills with a standard battery of achievement tests would indicate anything other than a global reading and spelling retardation among Retarded Readers.

Letter and Number Skills

Several measures from the Minnesota Test required knowledge of letters and numbers. The Retarded Readers were significantly deficient at the .05 level on tests of visual symbol recognition (Measure 58) and writing letters to dictation (Measure 85), but they did not differ significantly from Normal Readers on 4 other measures involving letter and number skills (Measures 47, 48, 83, and 84). These results do not suggest a severe deficiency of basic letter and number skills among Retarded Readers.

Visual Perceptual Speed for Verbal Material

The remaining 12 measures of skills directly related to reading were all timed tests where the score was either determined by the number of correct responses in a given time or the amount of time required to complete a given number of responses. In all cases the subject's task was to indicate his location or recognition of printed verbal material by making a response such as underlining, drawing a connecting line, or writing a coded symbol as rapidly as possible. Even though the majority of these measures involved relatively simple letter and number stimuli for which reading was not essential, the Normal Readers were significantly superior beyond the .001 level on 9 of the tests (Measures 18, 19, 20, 95, 96, 99, 100, 101, and 102), beyond the .01 level on 2 others (Measures 91 and 103), and there was no significant difference on only one task (Measure 97). These results indicate that the Retarded Readers did have particular difficulty on tasks requiring rapid responses to simple visual verbal stimuli. The rather curious fact that one of these tasks served as part of the criterion for equating the groups in nonverbal intelligence is discussed below. Also discussed in a later section is the deficiency of perceptual speed among Retarded Readers for measures with visual nonverbal input.

NONVERBAL INTELLIGENCE

The Retarded Readers and Normal Readers were essentially identical in Performance IQ (Measure 5) because this measure served as the criterion of normal nonverbal intelligence. The mean Performance IQ of both groups was 107. Performance IQ is based upon a summation of the weighted scores of five subtests. It might be assumed, therefore, that the groups would not differ significantly on any of these subtests. Although the difference between groups was not significant for the Picture Arrangement, Picture Completion, and Block Design subtests (Measures 14, 15, and 16), the Normal Readers were significantly superior (.001 level) to Retarded Readers on the Digit Symbol subtest (Measure 18), and the Retarded Readers were significantly superior (.01 level) to Normal Readers on the Object Assembly subtest (Measure 17).

The Digit Symbol Test was mentioned in the preceding section as one of the measures of visual perceptual speed on which the Retarded Readers were particularly deficient. In the present group of Retarded Readers this deficiency was very marked even though visual perceptual speed contributed about one fifth to the measure of nonverbal intelligence on which the groups were purposely equated. It is therefore quite evident that difficulty in maintaining a sustained rapid response to even very simple visual verbal material must occur frequently among children with reading problems.

The Digit Symbol Test requires the subject to inscribe symbols under printed digits as rapidly as possible on the basis of a code printed at the top of the test. This test is classified as a Performance subtest because it requires a manual rather than an oral response, but the visual input of the test should probably be classified as verbal rather than nonverbal. The findings of this study are in accordance with the findings of a number of investigations of the patterns of subtest scores of retarded readers on the Wechsler Intelligence Scale for Children, where a significant deficit on the Coding subtest (a measure which corresponds to the Digit Symbol subtest of the Wechsler-Bellevue Scale) was found to accompany deficiencies on the Verbal subtests of this intelligence scale (Altus, 1956; Burks and Bruce, 1955; Graham and Kamano, 1958; Robeck, 1960; and Sheldon and Garton, 1959). At least one other investigator, however, has not found a coding deficiency among retarded readers (Neville, 1961).

Performance IQ may not have been entirely appropriate as the criterion of nonverbal intelligence for the present study. To the extent that the Digit Symbol Test contributed to Performance IQ, the nonverbal intelligence of the Retarded Readers may have been underestimated relative to that of Normal Readers. Such a bias in the criterion of nonverbal intelligence could, in turn, result in an underestimation of the deficiencies of Retarded Readers. If the Retarded Readers had been equated with Normal Readers on the basis of a different criterion of nonverbal intelligence, the Retarded Readers may have been significantly deficient on an even higher proportion of the other measures in this study.

The significant superiority of Retarded Readers on the Object Assembly Test might suggest a special facility for this type of nonverbal manipulative task. Altus (1956) and Sheldon and Garton (1959) found that retarded readers showed the greatest proficiency in the Object Assembly subtest in relation to the other subtests of the Wechsler Intelligence Scale for Children. This task may involve tactual-kinesthetic skills of the variety required for the other measures on which Retarded Readers were significantly superior to Normal Readers (Table 7). It might also be conjectured that the Retarded Readers were normal only in the skills required by the Object Assembly Test, and that their non-reading deficit extended to the skills required by the remaining Performance subtests. If, however, the groups had been equated on the basis of their Object Assembly score alone the resulting group of Normal Readers would have been higher in Performance IQ as a consequence of the upward adjustment of the group's Object Assembly score. This would have undoubtedly increased the disparity between groups to the extent that there would be very few tests on which Retarded Readers were not significantly inferior to Normal Readers.

The results for the Performance subtests illustrate very clearly the pitfalls that can occur in attempts to define an area of normal intellectual functioning in connection with a so-called "specific" disability. This problem will be discussed at greater length in a later chapter. Fortunately, the differences between Retarded Readers and Normal Readers on several of the Performance subtests should not seriously hamper the interpretation of the results of this study. If anything, the nonverbal intelligence of Retarded Readers was underestimated. The finding of a significant deficit on many nonreading measures in a group of Retarded Readers with relatively high nonverbal intelligence serves to strengthen the indication of a lack of specificity of reading disability. This lack of specificity is probably the most important single finding of the present study.

VERBAL INTELLIGENCE

As discussed in the preceding section, the mean Performance IQ of both groups was 107, in the upper part of the region of "average" intelligence which extends through the range 91-110. The procedures for selecting Retarded Readers and Normal Readers placed no direct restrictions upon Verbal IQ. In such a case the mean Verbal IQ of Normal Readers should tend to equal their mean Performance IQ (Wechsler, 1944). If the reading disability of Retarded Readers were truly specific to reading, their Verbal IQ should also tend to equal their

Performance IQ, since no reading is directly required on any part of the Verbal scale except in the last 2 items of the Arithmetic subtest. The scores on most of the Verbal subtests could, of course, be affected by a deficiency of educational achievement secondary to reading disability.

The differences between groups on the Verbal IQ subtests are easier to interpret than the results for Performance IQ. Normal Readers were significantly superior to Retarded Readers on all 5 of the Verbal subtests (Measures 8-12) which contributed to Verbal IQ, plus an alternate Verbal subtest, the Vocabulary Test (Measure 13). The mean Verbal IQ of Normal Readers was 107, exactly the same as their mean Performance IQ; whereas the mean Verbal IQ of Retarded Readers was 87, 20 points below their mean Performance IQ, and in the region of "dull-normal" intelligence (Wechsler, 1944). These results indicate that the reading disability of the Retarded Readers was accompanied by severe deficiencies in the types of skill measured by the Verbal subtests of the Wechsler-Bellevue Intelligence Scale.

Verbal IQ was based upon a summation of the weighted scores of 5 Verbal subtests (Measures 8-12). A sixth Verbal subtest, the Vocabulary Test (Measure 13), was not used for the computation of Verbal IQ. The largest deficit among these 6 Verbal subtests occurred on the Information subtest (Measure 8). The statistical magnitude of the difference between groups was larger for this test than for any other nonreading measure except Word Rhyming (Measure 73). The severe deficit on this test of general information may largely reflect a retardation of educational achievement secondary to reading retardation. The same explanation might be given for the large deficit of Retarded Readers on the Arithmetic subtest (Measure 11).

The difference between groups on the Similarities Test (Measure 12), which requires the subject to state the semantic similarity of pairs of words, might be attributable to the educational handicap of the Retarded Readers, but could also reflect a more basic impairment of verbal concepts. Differences between groups on the Comprehension and Digit Span Tests (Measures 9 and 10) were of smaller statistical magnitude, but still significant beyond the .01 level. Once again, the deficit of Retarded Readers on these subtests could either be secondary to educational retardation or could be at least partially attributable to more basic impairment of verbal aptitude. The Comprehension Test requires oral evaluation of situations involving problems of human conduct. The Digit Span Test assesses a completely different verbal skill — the oral repetition of spoken digits. If the deficit of Retarded Readers on the Verbal subtests was entirely produced by their educational handicap, then it must be concluded that such a handicap has very widespread effects on verbal skills.

Oral vocabulary skills are usually considered to provide a good estimate of overall verbal aptitude. The Retarded Readers showed severe deficiency on the Wechsler Vocabulary Test (Measure 13), which requires oral definition of single words, and the Peabody Picture

Vocabulary Test (Measure 33), which simply requires the subject to indicate on each trial which of 4 pictures corresponds to a spoken word. According to the IQ norms of the Peabody Test the Retarded Readers obtained a mean IQ of 102, in contrast to a mean vocabulary IQ of 112 for Normal Readers (Measure 34). By this criterion the listening vocabulary of Retarded Readers could be considered relatively low, but within the normal range. The results for the Wechsler and Peabody Vocabulary Tests demonstrated an impairment of both speaking and listening vocabulary among Retarded Readers.

An alternate form of the Peabody Vocabulary Test was given in which the vocabulary words were presented in written rather than spoken form (Measure 35). This measure, which was one of the reading tasks on which Retarded Readers were most deficient, was intended to indicate the relationship between reading and listening vocabulary in each group. The mean reading vocabulary score of 97 words for Normal Readers almost equalled their mean listening vocabulary score of 101 words; while the reading vocabulary of Retarded Readers was 58 words in comparison with their mean listening vocabulary of 93 words (Appendix C). These findings provide a clear demonstration that the reading difficulty of Retarded Readers was not directly attributable to a limitation of spoken language.

The finding that the nonreading deficit of Retarded Readers includes the types of verbal skills sampled by the Verbal subtests of the Wechsler-Bellevue Scale and the Peabody Vocabulary Test is in accordance with the results of several other investigators (Graham and Kamano, 1958; Rabinovitch et al., 1954; Robeck, 1960; and Sheldon and Garton, 1959). Just how much of this verbal difficulty is secondary to the educational retardation produced by reading disability cannot be determined in this type of study. The possibility of interpreting this verbal deficit as evidence for dysfunction of the left cerebral hemisphere is discussed in a later section.

INPUT-OUTPUT CHARACTERISTICS

The input and output characteristics of tests which differentiated Normal and Retarded Readers and tests on which the groups did not differ significantly are shown in Tables 5, 6, and 7. Table 8 summarizes the results of the statistical analysis for measures in the various input and output categories. Within each category are indicated the number of measures on which Normal Readers were significantly superior, the number of measures on which Retarded Readers were significantly superior, and the number of measures on which the groups did not differ significantly.

Normal Readers showed the greatest statistical superiority to Retarded Readers on tests that required reading and spelling, but were also significantly superior on many tests that did not require either of these skills. Among these nonreading tests were measures that involved spoken (auditory verbal) input and spoken (verbal speech) output,

TABLE 8

Test results summarized according to input and output requirements, with an indication of the direction of statistical significance of the measures in each category.

INPUT		OUTPUT		Normal Readers Superior	Retarded Readers Superior	No Significant Difference
Visual (41)	Verbal (14)	Verbal (4)	Speech (2)	2		
			Writing (2)	1		1
		Nonverbal (10)	Manual (9)	8		1
			Choice (1)	1		
	Nonverbal (27)	Verbal (5)	Speech (3)			3
			Writing (2)	2		
		Nonverbal	Drawing (6)	2		4
			Manual (8)	5	1	2
			Choice (8)	4		4
Auditory (20)	Verbal (19)	Verbal (19)	Speech (16)	13		3
			Writing (3)	3		
		Nonverbal (0)				
	Nonverbal (1)	Verbal (0)				
		Nonverbal	Choice (1)	1		
Somesthetic (1)	Verbal (2)	Verbal (2)	Speech (2)			2
		Nonverbal (0)				
	Nonverbal (9)	Verbal (2)	Speech (2)		2	
		Nonverbal (7)	Manual (3)		2	1
			Choice (4)	1		3
No Input (16)		Verbal (5)	Speech (2)	1		1
			Writing (3)			3
		Nonverbal (11)	Drawing (3)	1		2
			Manual (6)	2		4
			Choice (2)			2
TOTAL				47	5	36

and measures that involved pictorial or figural (visual nonverbal) input and nonverbal (manual, drawing, or choice) output. Thus, the Retarded Readers were not only deficient in nonreading *verbal* tasks, as discussed in the preceding section, but were also deficient on nonreading *visual* tasks.

The measures on which Normal and Retarded Readers did not differ significantly included many tasks with visual nonverbal input or with only instructional input. These results could not be considered unexpected. If the Retarded Readers were to equal Normal Readers at all, it should be on tasks with no verbal requirements. There were, however, several measures on which the lack of difference was unexpected. These included the word association test (Measure 105) and the lateral dominance tests (Measures 51-53).

The small number of measures for which Retarded Readers were significantly superior to Normal Readers included, in addition to the previously mentioned Object Assembly Test, 4 tests (Measures 22, 24, 49, and 50) with somesthetic input. This suggests the possible operation of some sort of compensatory mechanism.

Input Characteristics

Verbal and Nonverbal Input. Tables 4 (p. 27) and 8 (p. 49) list 35 measures with verbal input and 37 measures with nonverbal input. The results of analysis of covariance for these measures can be summarized as follows:

	Normal Readers Superior	Retarded Readers Superior	No Significant Difference
Verbal Input	28	0	7
Nonverbal Input	15	5	17

The Normal Readers were superior on the majority of verbal-input measures, including both printed (visual verbal) and spoken (auditory verbal) stimuli. The groups did not differ significantly on Fingertip Number Writing (Measures 47 and 48), the only measure involving somesthetic verbal input. On 3 of the other nonsignificant verbal-input tasks (Measures 69, 71, and 83), the high proportion of perfect performances in both groups reduced the meaningfulness of statistical comparison.

There were 2 verbal-input measures with adequately distributed scores on which the groups did not significantly differ. These were the Word Association Test (Measure 106) and a test of visual perceptual speed which required the subject to underline 2 separate printed letters interspersed among a page of printed letters (Measure 97). The Word Association Test was scored in terms of the grammatical conformity between stimulus words and response words, and the lack of difference between groups for this test (the Retarded Readers actually obtained a higher mean score) suggests that the Retarded Readers were not deficient in basic habits of grammatical usage. The lack of difference between groups on the two-letter perceptual speed task is somewhat anomalous, since the Normal Readers were significantly superior on all of the other verbal-input tasks of the perceptual speed series. This particular task of discriminating 2 separate letters may require some additional nonverbal skill. It must be concluded that Retarded Readers were unquestionably deficient in the majority of sampled skills with verbal input.

The superiority of Normal Readers was much less marked for the tasks with nonverbal input. Even so, the Retarded Readers were significantly deficient on 15, or about 40 percent, of the nonverbal-input measures. Of these, 2 (Measures 86 and 90) depended upon reading ability, since they required a written response to pictorial stimuli; 11 involved a nonverbal response to visual nonverbal stimuli and will be discussed more fully in later sections; and one, the Rhythm Test (Measure 27), required a choice response to nonverbal auditory stimuli. All 5 of the tests in which Retarded Readers were significantly superior (Measures 16, 22, 24, 49, and 50) involved nonverbal input, and will be discussed below. Of the 16 tasks with nonverbal input on which the groups did not differ significantly, 10 had visual input. Thus, the 11 visual nonverbal skills on which Retarded Readers were deficient were balanced by 10 visual nonverbal skills in which the groups did not differ. In summary, the Retarded Readers were superior to Normal Readers on a small number of measures with nonverbal input, with an equal balance on the remaining nonverbal-input tasks between measures on which Retarded Readers were deficient and measures on which Retarded and Normal Readers did not differ.

Sensory Input. There were 41 measures with visual input, 20 with auditory input, 11 with somesthetic input, and 16 with no sensory input other than initial instructions. The results summarized according to sensory input were as follows:

	Normal Readers Superior	*Retarded Readers Superior*	*No Significant Difference*
Visual	25	1	15
Auditory	17	0	3
Somesthetic	1	4	6
No Sensory Input	4	0	12

The Retarded Readers were superior only on the Object Assembly Test, and the Normal Readers were superior on two thirds of the remaining tests with visual input. These included reading tasks, while the visual tasks on which the groups did not differ included several subtests of the Wechsler Performance Scale.

The Retarded Readers were deficient on an even higher proportion of measures with auditory input than with visual input. Both groups performed almost perfectly in answering simple spoken questions (Measure 71) and in a simple sentence completion task (Measure 69); and the groups did not differ in Word Association (Measure 106), as discussed in the preceding section. The deficiency of Retarded Readers on the remaining 85 percent of auditory-input tasks, as compared with 63 percent of visual tasks, does not necessarily indicate a more pronounced auditory deficit. It will be noted that all but one of the auditory tasks were verbal, and thus the auditory deficiency of Retarded Readers cannot be separated from the verbal deficit discussed in the preceding section. However, the Retarded Readers were also extremely deficient on the one nonverbal auditory test, the Rhythm Test (Measure

27). This test, which had no verbal component, required discrimination of complex auditory patterns. It is unfortunate that more tests with auditory nonverbal input were not given.

The one type of sensory input for which Retarded Readers tended to be superior was somesthetic input. The Halstead Tactual Performance Test requires the subject to place blocks in a formboard while blindfolded. The Retarded Readers were greatly superior on the initial trial for this test, using the preferred hand (Measure 22); the groups did not differ significantly on the second trial, which requires use of the nonpreferred hand (Measure 23); and the Retarded Readers were barely superior on the final trial, using both hands (Measure 24). The Retarded Readers were also barely superior (.05 level) in tactile form recognition with each hand while blindfolded (Measures 49 and 50). The other somesthetic-input tasks on which the groups did not differ significantly were recognition of numbers written on the fingertips (Measures 47 and 48), tactile suppression with double simultaneous stimulation (Measures 41 and 42), and tactile identification of fingers of the right hand (Measure 45). The Normal Readers were barely superior (.05 level) in tactile identification of fingers of the left hand (Measure 46). Thus, the Retarded Readers were more proficient than Normal Readers in several tasks with somesthetic input, but this superiority did not extend to all somesthetic tasks.

The two groups did not differ significantly on the majority of tests which had no sensory input other than initial instructions. These included 3 tasks which required a verbal response, expression of ideas (Measure 74), and speed of writing the name with preferred and nonpreferred hands (Measures 56 and 57). Also, both groups exhibited almost perfect accuracy in writing the numbers 1 to 20 in sequence (Measure 84). The groups did not differ in nonverbal drawing responses on the Tactual Performance Test (Measures 25 and 26) and in drawing a house (Measure 79), in tapping speed with either hand (Measures 29 and 30), in time judgment (Measure 32), or in lateral dominance (Measures 51 and 53). However, the Retarded Readers were quite deficient in sequential naming of months (Measure 70) and in drawing a man (Measure 80), and somewhat less deficient in strength of hand grip (Measures 54 and 55).

When results were interpreted on the basis of sensory input, the Retarded Readers were deficient in almost all auditory-input tasks, on almost two thirds of the visual-input tasks, and on about one fourth of the tasks which involved no sensory input. On all but one of the tasks with somesthetic input the Retarded Readers were either equal or superior to Normal Readers. It must be concluded, therefore, that the deficiency of Retarded Readers was most pronounced on tasks with visual and auditory input.

Output Characteristics

Verbal and nonverbal output. When the mode of response was classified as a function of verbal and nonverbal requirements there were 37 measures with verbal output and 51 with nonverbal output. These results are summarized as follows:

	Normal Readers Superior	Retarded Readers Superior	No Significant Difference
Verbal Output	22	2	13
Nonverbal Output	25	3	23

The Normal Readers were superior on about 60 percent of the tasks with verbal output and on about 50 percent of the tasks with nonverbal output. Of the 5 tests on which Retarded Readers were superior, 2 had verbal output and 3 had nonverbal output. Thus, the Retarded Readers seemed to be almost as deficient on tests involving nonverbal output as on tests involving verbal output. These results will be clarified by a discussion of more specific response modes. It will be recalled that speaking and writing are exclusively verbal response categories, whereas drawing, manual, and choice responses are exclusively nonverbal categories.

Response modality of output. With the further specification of response modality the 37 verbal output tasks can be subdivided into 27 tasks requiring spoken responses and 10 requiring written responses; and the 51 tasks with nonverbal output can be subdivided into 26 tasks requiring manual response, 9 requiring a drawing response, and 16 requiring choice responses. The summary of results classified in this manner is as follows:

	Normal Readers Superior	Retarded Readers Superior	No Significant Difference
Verbal Output			
Speech	16	2	9
Writing	6	0	4
Nonverbal Output			
Manual	15	3	8
Drawing	3	0	6
Choice	7	0	9

Normal Readers were superior on about 60 percent of the tests with speech output. Of the 16 speech-output tests on which Normal Readers were superior, 13 had auditory verbal input. This suggests that the speaking deficiency of Retarded Readers was largely limited to tasks which required a spoken response to a spoken stimulus. Except for oral spelling the most severe deficiency in speech input-speech output exhibited by Retarded Readers occurred on a simple rhyming task (Measure 73). This deficiency would have been even more striking if the maximum score had not been restricted to 5 rhyming words per stimulus word. The other tasks involving speech input-speech output on which Normal Readers were superior ranged from relatively simple echoic tasks such as articulation (Measure 68), Wechsler Digit Span (Measure 10), and Sentence Repetition (Measure 60), to more complex tasks such as the remaining Wechsler Verbal subtests, retelling a spoken paragraph (Measure 77), and answering questions about a spoken paragraph (Measure 62). Of the 3 remaining speech-output tasks on which Normal Readers were superior, 2 were reading tasks with visual-verbal input, and the other was a sequential naming task with only instructional input. On the latter test (Measure 70) the Retarded Readers made a surprisingly large number of errors in naming the months in correct order. The 9 speech-output tasks on which the groups did not differ significantly were distributed fairly evenly among input categories, and included such various tasks as Wechsler Picture Completion (Measure 15), sentence completion (Measure 69), naming pictures (Measure 72), fingertip number writing (Measures 47 and 48), and word association (Measure 106).

Since all writing tasks presuppose some reading ability, the superiority of Normal Readers on most of these tasks was not surprising. The groups did not differ on several simple writing tasks including speed of writing the name (Measures 56 and 57), writing letters (Measure 83), and writing numbers (Measure 84).

The Normal Readers were also superior on over half of the 26 tests which required manual responses. This finding was rather unexpected, since the normal nonverbal intelligence of Retarded Readers might be expected to extend to a variety of manual tasks. Of the 15 manual tasks on which Normal Readers were superior, 12 were tests of visual perceptual speed. The Retarded Readers were deficient in speed of visual perception for tasks with both verbal (Measures 91, 95, 96, 99, and 100-103) and nonverbal (Measures 92-94) input. The remaining manual deficiencies of Retarded Readers were in a timing response (Measure 31) and strength of grip (Measures 54 and 55). Retarded Readers were superior in Object Assembly and in the 2 Tactual Performance Test measures. The manual tasks on which the groups did not differ significantly included 2 of the Performance subtests (Measures 14 and 16), one visual perceptual speed test (Measure 97), 2 parts of the Tactual Performance Test (Measures 23 and 26), tapping speed (Measures 29 and 30), and time judgment (Measure 32). In general, the Retarded Readers seemed to have particular difficulty on those manual tasks which required rapid eye-hand coordination, regardless of the verbal content of the visual stimuli.

A total of 9 drawing tasks were presented, of which 6 involved copying and 3 required drawing from memory. The Retarded Readers were deficient in copying a cross (Measure 37), copying a complex figure (Measure 78), and drawing a man from memory (Measure 80). The reasons for deficiency in these particular drawings are not clear. It should be noted, however, that deficient copying of the Greek cross is characteristic of certain cerebral lesions (Kløve and Reitan, 1958), and that difficulty in drawing a man has been found in previous studies of children with reading disability (cf., Cohn, 1961). On the remaining drawing tasks the performance of Retarded Readers was quite comparable to that of Normal Readers, indicating that reading disability was not accompanied by gross incoordination.

The Retarded Readers were deficient on almost half of the 16 tasks which required choice responses. Since the choice responses required no special manual or oral skill, a deficiency on these tasks should be indicative of an input or central difficulty, and should tend to eliminate any possibility that reading disability is a purely expressive disorder in the present group. The 7 choice tasks on which Retarded Readers were deficient included a visual-verbal reading task (Measure 66), 4 visual-nonverbal tasks (Measures 21, 105, 108, and 109) which required discrimination of complex figures, an auditory nonverbal discrimination task (Measure 27), and a somesthetic discrimination task (Measure 46). The choice tasks on which the groups did not differ tended to be less complex and included 4 measures of visual and tactile suppression (Measures 41-44), a visual form matching task (Measure 63), a color form test (Measure 107), a somesthetic discrimination task (Measure 45), and 2 lateral dominance tests (Measures 51 and 53). It is especially noteworthy that the Retarded Readers were severely deficient in discriminating reversed line drawings (Measure 105), and that their performance of the Halstead Category Test (Measure 21), found by Reitan (1955) to be the best single measure of the Halstead Battery for differentiating brain damaged from non-brain-damaged adults, was considerably less deficient than their performance of many other tasks.

Unclassified Tasks

The groups were statistically compared on 12 measures which were not included, because of complex input, in the classifications presented in Tables 4 and 8. All of these measures are, however, included in the tabulations according to statistical significance in Tables 5, 6, and 7. The Retarded Readers were significantly deficient beyond the .001 level on 7 of the complex-input tests, beyond the .05 level on 3 of the tests, and the groups did not differ significantly on the remaining 2 tests. On the 4 tests which required some form of reading the Retarded Readers were almost as deficient in choosing among pictures in response to printed words on Form A of the Peabody Picture Vocabulary Test (Measure 35, a choice response to a combined verbal-nonverbal visual input) as they had been in the Oral Reading Criterion (Measure 1). They were also very deficient in making a choice among printed syllables in response to a spoken syllable on the Halstead Speech Perception Test (Measure 28, a choice response to combined visual-auditory verbal input), and the high proportion of perfect performances among Normal Readers probably attenuated the deficiency of Retarded Readers in matching printed words to pictures (Measure 64, visual verbal and nonverbal input, nonverbal choice output) and in matching printed words to spoken words (Measure 65, auditory and visual verbal input, nonverbal choice output).

On 4 tasks which required response to printed letters or numbers, the Retarded Readers were very deficient on 2 tests which required sequential connection of separated symbols (Measures 19 and 20, visual verbal and nonverbal input, nonverbal manual output) and on a visual number-symbol coding task, the Wechsler Digit Symbol subtest (Measure 18, visual verbal and nonverbal input, nonverbal drawing output); but were less deficient in choosing among printed letters in response to a spoken letter (Measure 58, auditory and visual verbal input, nonverbal choice output).

The nonreading task with complex input on which Retarded Readers were most deficient was Picture Vocabulary (Measure 29, auditory verbal and visual nonverbal input, nonverbal choice output), which demonstrated an impairment of listening vocabulary that could not be attributed to difficulty in oral expression. The remaining nonreading task on which Retarded Readers were barely deficient was spatial orientation (Measure 104), which required manual orientative responses to both visual nonverbal and auditory verbal stimuli.

The 2 tasks on which the groups did not differ significantly involved sequential pointing and sequential manipulation of visual stimuli in response to auditory verbal stimuli. These were Retention Span (Measure 59) and Following Directions (Measure 61).

Summary of Input and Output Characteristics

As Table 8 (p. 49) shows, the disability of Retarded Readers was not sharply limited to any specific input or output categories. Oral reading, the criterion which defined reading disability, involves visual verbal input and verbal speech output. The most consistent deficiency occurred on tasks with visual verbal input, regardless of output requirements, and in almost all of the tasks requiring a written output. However, the *visual* deficiency of Retarded Readers extended to about half of the tasks with visual nonverbal input despite the fact that the groups had been equated in nonverbal intelligence on the basis of a set of tasks with visual nonverbal input; and the *verbal* deficiency of Retarded Readers extended to a large proportion of tasks with auditory verbal input.

The apparent regions of normal functioning for Retarded Readers included the type of visual nonverbal tasks for which the 2 groups had been equated by the criterion of nonverbal intelligence, a number of tasks with nonverbal output, and a number of tasks with no sensory input requirements. There was also a definite indication of above normal performance on several tests with somesthetic input.

When test results are interpreted on the basis of input and output characteristics, then, the reading disability of Retarded Readers seems to be systematically nonspecific, with greatest deficiency occurring in the form of an interaction of visual and verbal disabilities. In this type of analysis the central processes between input and output were not specified. These additional aspects of test performance, which could provide further insight into the extent of disability in Retarded Readers, will be discussed in the following sections.

TEST RESULTS INDICATIVE
OF CEREBRAL DYSFUNCTION

Estimates of cerebral dysfunction based on impressionistic analyses of the nonreading test results of individual subjects will be presented in Chapter 7. The differences between groups for some of these tests are discussed in the present section.

Lateralized Cerebral Dysfunction

The 2 kinds of evidence for lateralized cerebral deficit to be dealt with here are discrepancy between verbal and nonverbal abilities and selective impairment of one side of the body. The verbal-nonverbal discrepancy is best assessed by the comparison of Verbal IQ and Performance IQ, and the unilateral impairment of bodily functioning can be assessed by measures in which the 2 sides of the body were tested separately.

Verbal-nonverbal discrepancy. A number of investigators have reported an association between low Verbal IQ and lesions of the left (or "dominant") cerebral hemisphere, and between low Performance IQ and lesions of the right (or "nondominant") hemisphere in studies where the Wechsler-Bellevue Intelligence Scale was administered to adults with brain damage (Anderson, 1951; Bauer and Becka, 1954; Costa and Vaughan, 1962; Doehring, Reitan, and Kløve, 1961; Heilbrun, 1956; Kløve, 1959; McFie, 1961; Matthews and Reitan, 1964; Morrow and Mark, 1955; Reed and Reitan, 1963; Reitan, 1955; Stark, 1961). The difference between the mean Verbal IQ of 87 and the mean Performance IQ of 107 for Retarded Readers must be regarded as something other than a chance variation, especially in view of the equality of Verbal and Performance IQ in Normal Readers. As mentioned in a preceding section, however, the occurrence of a disparity between verbal and nonverbal abilities in Retarded Readers might be attributable to the educational handicap imposed by reading difficulty, whereas the studies of patients with brain damage usually involve adults whose lesions were acquired after normal educational opportunity. In evaluating the probability of lateralized cerebral lesions, Reitan and his associates (Reitan, 1959; 1965) usually require other evidence in addition to a discrepancy between Verbal IQ and Performance IQ. Although the Verbal-Performance IQ difference in Retarded Readers is of the same order of magnitude as observed in adults with left hemisphere lesions, such a finding by itself does not constitute *de facto* evidence of lateralized cerebral dysfunction among Retarded Readers.

Unilateral sensory and motor impairment. Several different aspects of unilateral function are evaluated in the Indiana Neuropsychology Battery. A large deficiency for one side of the body is indicative of a lesion involving the contralateral cerebral hemisphere in all cases where there is no evidence of peripheral involvement. The motor skills for which each side of the body was separately assessed included the Tapping Test (Measures 29 and 30), the Tactual Performance Test (Measures 22 and 23), strength of grip (Measures 54 and 55), and speed of writing (Measures 56 and 57). Measures of lateralized sensory and perceptual abilities included tactile suppression and visual suppression (Measures 41-44), finger agnosia (Measures 45 and 46), finger tip number writing (Measures 47 and 48), and tactile form recognition (Measures 49 and 50). To support the possibility of left hemisphere dysfunction suggested by the low Verbal IQ of Retarded Readers, there should have been some signs of lateralized impairment of the right side of the body in this group. Examination of the group means in Appendix C reveals no sign of unilateral weakness or poor sensitivity among Retarded Readers as compared with Normal Readers. This finding was confirmed by the reanalysis of test results with left-handed subjects eliminated. Since a variety of different motor and sensory skills were sampled, the evidence for a lack of unilateral sensory or motor impairment among Retarded Readers seems quite convincing.

The results for Retarded Readers do not conform to the pattern of test scores that would be predicted for adults with acquired lesions of the left cerebral hemisphere. There was no evidence of lateralized sensory or motor impairment, and the low Verbal IQ of Retarded Readers could be a result of the educational handicap imposed by reading disability.

Nonlateralized Cerebral Dysfunction

In assessing the probability of nonlateralized cerebral dysfunction, our intention was to examine the results of tests which have been found to differentiate reliably between patients with brain damage, regardless of the degree of lateralization, and patients without brain damage. An Impairment Index can be calculated from the scores of Halstead's tests, with the magnitude of the index determined by the number of tests for which the individual's score falls beyond the cutting score for that test. This index provides a reliable indicator of brain damage in adults (Reitan, 1955). Although the cutting scores developed for adults were not applicable in the present study, the statistical comparisons of Retarded Readers and Normal Readers for component tests of the Impairment Index provided a further indication of whether the pattern of deficit in Retarded Readers approximated that of adults with brain damage. The following results were obtained for measures which contribute to the Impairment Index:

Measure	Result of Statistical Comparison
21. Category Test	Normal Readers superior, .01 level
22. Tactual Performance Test, Preferred Hand	Retarded Readers superior, .001 level
23. Tactual Performance Test, Nonpreferred Hand	Not significant
24. Tactual Performance Test, Both Hands	Retarded Readers superior, .05 level
25. Tactual Performance Test, Memory	Not significant
26. Tactual Performance Test, Location	Not significant
27. Rhythm Test	Normal Readers superior, .001 level
28. Speech Perception Test	Normal Readers superior, .001 level
29. Tapping Test, Preferred Hand	Not significant
32. Time Sense Test, Memory Component	Not significant

An actual computation of the Impairment Index would have required summation of Measures 22, 23, and 24, for which the Retarded Readers would have remained superior. The "score" for Retarded Readers on the Impairment Index would then be a significant deficiency on 3 measures (one of which required reading), no impairment for 4 measures, and significant superiority for one measure. Therefore, despite the widespread nonreading deficit of Retarded Readers, there was no consistent impairment on a set of measures which are reliable indicators of cerebral lesions in adults.

The above examinations of the results for certain measures from the Indiana Neuropsychology Battery revealed no striking similarities between the deficiencies of Retarded Readers and those of adults with either lateralized or nonlateralized cerebral lesions. This cannot be interpreted as unequivocal evidence of normal cerebral functioning in Retarded Readers. It is obvious that the effects of congenital or long-standing lesions in children could differ in a number of respects from the effects of acquired lesions in adults. It is also possible that the grouping of data could mask indications of cerebral deficit that might be revealed by examination of the test profiles of individual Retarded Readers. For the present, however, it must be concluded that the nonreading disability of Retarded Readers did not show any strong resemblance to the effects of acquired cerebral lesions in adults.

INDICATIONS OF APHASIA

The use of 2 different aphasia examinations in this study permitted a thorough evaluation of the language deficit of Retarded Readers in relation to that of adults with brain damage classified as aphasic. The modified Halstead-Wepman Aphasia Examination has been used as part of the Indiana Neuropsychology Battery for prediction of the locus, extent, and type of cerebral lesion in patients whose neurological status is unknown at the time of testing (Reitan, 1965); whereas the Minnesota Test for Differential Diagnosis of Aphasia is commonly used to obtain a more complete description of language and related nonlanguage pathology in patients with known brain damage (Schuell, Jenkins, and Jimenez-Pabon, 1964). Both of these tests, like most other aphasia examinations, are designed in such a way that a person with unimpaired language abilities will obtain a perfect score on the majority of items. As a result, the distribution of scores for a normal group will be restricted by a large number of perfect or near-perfect scores. Many of the restricted distributions in this study occurred on aphasia subtests, and a number of aphasia subtests were not statistically analyzed because of the high proportion of errorless scores. The occurrence of such restricted distributions in both the Normal and Retarded Reader groups provides some indication in itself that the language impairment of Retarded Readers was not as severe or widespread as the language impairment of many adult aphasics.

Modified Halstead-Wepman
Aphasia Screening Test

The modified Halstead-Wepman Test is given as part of the Indiana Neuropsychology Battery to provide supporting evidence of language and nonlanguage pathology, and is usually scored simply by a notation of the presence or absence of the various symptoms of aphasia and associated disturbances. The results of this examination alone have been successfully used to predict the presence and the laterality of brain damage (Wheeler and Reitan, 1962).

The main symptoms of language impairment which can be inferred from the modified Halstead-Wepman Test are visual letter and number dysgnosia, dyslexia (visual word dysgnosia), auditory verbal dysgnosia, dysnomia (naming dyspraxia), spelling dyspraxia, dysgraphia (writing dyspraxia), dyscalculia (calculation dyspraxia), and central dysarthria (enunciatory dyspraxia). The main nonlanguage symptoms are visual form dysgnosia, construction dyspraxia, ideokinetic dyspraxia, and right-left disorientation. For the majority of these symptoms no statistical analysis of the difference between groups was carried out, and the results are presented in terms of comparative incidence of individual symptoms.

There was no indication of letter or number dysgnosia (difficulty in reading letters and numbers) in either group. The majority of

Retarded Readers made errors indicating dyslexia (difficulty in reading words, phrases, and sentences), with 33 of the 39 making at least one error and 21 making 2 or more errors on 5 items involving reading, whereas 33 of the 39 Normal Readers made no errors on these items. Neither group made errors indicative of auditory verbal dysgnosia (difficulty in understanding spoken verbal material) or dysnomia (difficulty in naming familiar objects), and both groups made about the same proportion of errors on the 4 items which reflected dysarthria (difficulty in oral articulation). On 3 spelling dyspraxia (difficulty in spelling) items, only 3 of the 39 Retarded Readers made no errors, as compared with 34 of the 39 Normal Readers. A high proportion of Retarded Readers also had difficulty on the 2 calculation (dyscalculia) items. Although many of the Retarded Readers exhibited handwriting that would probably be classified as dysgraphia (difficulty in the mechanics of handwriting) in adults, no objective measure of this symptom was obtained. The handwriting of many of the Normal Readers was also of poor quality, as would be expected for males in this age range.

With regard to nonlanguage symptoms, neither group showed any signs of visual form dysgnosia (difficulty in recognizing familiar objects) or ideokinetic dyspraxia (difficulty in the performance of habitual movements). On the 2 items indicative of right-left disorientation, 21 of the Retarded Readers and 29 of the Normal Readers made no errors (Normal Readers were significantly superior at the .05 level on Measure 104, a more elaborate test of spatial orientation). The 4 items indicative of construction dyspraxia (difficulty in copying nonverbal figures) were quantitatively scored by procedures described in Chapter 5. The groups did not differ significantly on 3 of the drawings (Measures 36, 38, and 39), but the Normal Readers were superior at the .05 level on the fourth item, copying a Greek cross (Measure 37), the item considered to be the most sensitive indicator of construction dyspraxia (Heimburger and Reitan, 1961).

The only marked symptoms of language disorder disclosed by the comparison of Normal and Retarded Readers on the modified Halstead-Wepman Test were dyslexia and spelling dyspraxia, both directly related to reading difficulty, and dyscalculia, which was probably attributable to the educational handicap of Retarded Readers. A possible symptom of dysgraphia was not adequately evaluated. The only suggestion of nonlanguage impairment was a barely significant superiority of Normal Readers in copying a Greek cross.

On this aphasia screening test, then, the only obvious symptoms exhibited by Retarded Readers involved skills that would be directly affected by reading retardation.

Modified Minnesota Test for Differential Diagnosis of Aphasia

The Minnesota Aphasia Test has been used to evaluate the extent and severity of language and associated nonlanguage disorders in patients with brain damage. The selection of therapeutic procedures may be largely guided by test findings, and the test may then be read-ministered to assess the patient's status during the course of therapy (Schuell, Jenkins, and Jimenez-Pabon, 1954). The majority of subtests were given in the modified form of the test that was used in the present study. In some instances equivalent measures from Wechsler-Bellevue subtests or from other tests of the Indiana Neuropsychology Battery were substituted, as indicated in Appendix A. The results for subtests in the various categories of language and nonlanguage disturbance are given below.

Auditory disturbances. Except for an initial auditory screening test, which was not given, all of the tests of auditory disturbance in-volved auditory verbal input. Both groups were essentially errorless on a simple test of word recognition (unnumbered), in identifying items named serially (Measure 59), and in carrying out spoken directions in correct order (Measure 61). The Retarded Readers were deficient in identifying printed letters in response to spoken letters (Measure 58), probably because of the visual verbal component of the task. However, the Retarded Readers were also deficient in repetition of spoken digits (Wechsler Bellevue Digit Span subtest, Measure 10), sentence repetition (Measure 60), and comprehension of a spoken paragraph (Measure 62), all of which had exclusively auditory verbal input. On the Minnesota Aphasia Test, then, the Retarded Readers did show signs of auditory verbal disturbances.

Visual and reading disturbances. The 2 groups did not differ on the one nonverbal visual task, which required matching of forms (Mea-sure 63). All of the remaining subtests in this part of the Minnesota Test involved visual verbal input, and thus required some form of reading. As would be expected, the Retarded Readers were deficient on all of these tasks.

Speech and language disturbances. All of these tests required verbal speech output, and the majority also involved auditory verbal input. The Retarded Readers were very inconsistent on these tests, performing 5 in a perfectly normal manner and showing pronounced impairment on 7 others. They were deficient on a simple articulation test (Measure 68), making an average of 2.4 errors of articulation in comparison with 0.8 errors by Normal Readers. On 6 tasks catego-rized as word-finding tests, both groups approached perfect perfor-mance in sentence completion (Measure 69), response to questions (Measure 71), and naming (Measure 72); but the Retarded Readers were very deficient in serial responses (Measure 70), rhyming (Measure 73), and definitions (Wechsler-Bellevue Vocabulary subtest, Measure 13). The largest statistical difference found for any single task that did not require reading or spelling was difficulty in rhyming words (Table 5, p. 40), with 24 of the Normal Readers and none of the Retarded Readers obtaining perfect scores. On the serial response task both groups were nearly perfect in counting to 20 and naming days of the week, but 25 of the Retarded Readers made 2 or more errors in naming the months of the year in correct order. For 3 tests categorized as functional speech, the groups did not differ significantly in expressing ideas (Measure 74) or in the total number of words used to describe a picture (Measure 75), but the Retarded Readers were very deficient in giving information (Wechsler-Bellevue Information subtest, Measure 8). Although the expressive quality of the picture description was not quantitatively assessed, the stories told by Retarded Readers seemed to be within normal limits for boys of their age. The Retarded Readers were slightly deficient in the simple formulation of sentences (Measure 76), and very deficient in more complex formulation tasks involving similarities (Wechsler Bellevue Similarities subtest, Measure 12) and retelling a paragraph (Measure 77). On the tests of speech and language disturbances, then, the Retarded Readers appeared to be normal in some of the more simple habits of spoken language, and quite deficient in certain complex habits of spoken language.

Visuomotor and writing disturbances. This category included a variety of verbal and nonverbal tasks, with all but one requiring either a drawing or a writing response. The results of the drawing tests were evenly split. There was no significant difference between groups for the 2 relatively simple tasks of drawing a house (Measure 79) and reproducing a wheel (Measure 81), but the Retarded Readers were very deficient in copying a complex figure (Measure 78) and drawing a man (Measure 81). In object assembly (Wechsler Object Assembly subtest, Measure 17), as discussed previously, the Retarded Readers were significantly superior. On 6 of the 8 tests which required written responses the Retarded Readers were significantly deficient. The 2 measures on which their performance was relatively normal were reproducing letters (Measure 83) and writing sequential numbers (Measure 84). The severe deficiency of Retarded Readers in oral spelling (Measure 87) equalled their deficiency in written spelling (Measure 2). On this group of tests which emphasized verbal and nonverbal response skills, then, the Retarded Readers were superior to Normal Readers for one nonverbal manual task and did not differ from Normal Readers on 2 drawing tasks, but were deficient on 2 other drawing tasks and on 9 tests which required writing and spelling.

Numerical relations and arithmetic processes. The 7 subtests in this category were not given, but it is quite evident from the results of the Wechsler-Bellevue Arithmetic subtest (Measure 11) that the Retarded Readers were very deficient in arithmetic and related abilities. Whether this is a basic impairment or whether it is secondary to reading retardation cannot be determined within the framework of the present study.

In striking contrast to the results of the modified Halstead-Wepman Aphasia Screening Test, where the only marked deficiency of Retarded Readers was on tasks directly related to reading or spelling, the Retarded Readers showed severe deficiencies within each of the 5 areas of functioning sampled by the modified Minnesota Test for Differential Diagnosis of Aphasia. Within each area, the Retarded Readers tended to function at a normal level for the relatively simple skills and below normal for more complex skills. Of the 5 major diagnostic categories of aphasia in adults proposed by Schuell, Jenkins, and Jimenez-Pabon (1964), the pattern exhibited by Retarded Readers seems most similar to Group 2: "Aphasia complicated by central involvement of visual processes." However, the pattern of visual and verbal deficit exhibited by Retarded Readers in comparison to Normal Readers was probably more irregular than would be the case for aphasic adults in comparison to nonaphasic adults.

The most likely explanation for the occurrence of more pronounced aphasic symptoms on the Minnesota Test than on the Halstead-Wepman Test is that the former test is more thorough. It samples a greater range of difficulty than the latter, which was designed as a brief screening procedure. This finding suggests that reading disability may involve a subtle language disturbance of the same general nature as that exhibited by aphasic adults; and the pattern of combined visual and verbal disturbance does conform in general outline to a specific type of aphasia postulated by Schuell *et al*. As mentioned before, however, there is one important difference between the language impairment of retarded readers and that of aphasic adults. In adults aphasia can be classified as a difficulty in retrieving previously acquired language skills, whereas reading disability seems to be characterized by difficulty in the initial acquisition of certain language skills.

TEST RESULTS RELEVANT TO THEORETICAL EXPLANATIONS OF READING DISABILITY

The results of the statistical comparisons of groups for individual tests can be interpreted as evidence for or against some of the theoretical explanations of specific reading disability discussed in previous chapters. Such interpretations require the assumption that the measures of this study provided a suitable test for a particular theory, plus the additional assumption that the Retarded Readers in this study were an appropriate group for representing the type of reading disability to which a given theory referred.

Directional Confusion and Gerstmann's Syndrome

Hermann's hypothesis (1959) that disturbance of directional function acts as a specific factor in causing congenital word-blindness or constitutional dyslexia was not strongly upheld by the results of the present study. The difference between groups on a fairly extensive test of right-left orientation (Measure 104) was barely significant, in contrast to the many skills in which Retarded Readers were severely deficient. It does not seem reasonable to suppose that such a relatively mild deficit would have severe and widespread consequences.

Hermann also concluded that constitutional dyslexia and Gerstmann's syndrome have so many features in common that these 2 conditions are probably both produced by the same fundamental disturbance of directional function. According to Hermann, the most important symptoms of Gerstmann's syndrome are right-left disorientation, finger agnosia, acalculia, and agraphia. The Retarded Readers of the present study showed mild right-left disorientation (Measure 104), mild finger agnosia for one hand only (Measure 46), and severe calculation difficulty (Measure 11). Although agraphia was not quantitatively assessed, a number of the Retarded Readers exhibited handwriting quite similar to the examples of dysgraphia given by Hermann. However, these symptoms constituted only a small portion of the deficient performances by Retarded Readers.

It can be concluded that the pattern of deficit of Retarded Readers was much more widespread than the pattern of symptomatology described by Hermann as characteristic of constitutional dyslexia or congenital word-blindness. The results of the present study cannot be interpreted as supporting Hermann's explanation of the causes of specific reading disability.

Lateral Dominance and Strephosymbolia

Although Orton's theory (Orton, 1937) could not be directly tested, certain characteristics of retarded readers postulated by the theory were evaluated. The failure of hemispheric dominance which was thought by Orton to underlie reading disability was said to involve inconsistencies of hand, foot, and eye preference. This was certainly not true of the present group of Retarded Readers, since one of the few areas of functioning in which they did not differ from Normal Readers was in hand, eye, and foot preference (Measures 51, 52, and 53). However, it is possible that the Retarded Readers were too old to exhibit incomplete dominance. Several writers (Benton, 1959; Harris, 1961) have suggested that incomplete dominance involves a delay of neurological maturation and is exhibited most strikingly in younger children.

Manifestations of strephosymbolia more directly related to reading are reversal of letters in reading and mirror writing. The reading and writing errors of Retarded Readers appeared to be unsystematic, with no observed tendencies toward reversals or mirror writing. However, there was a significant deficit on a test which required discrimination of reversed figures (Measure 105).

In general, the results of the present study did not provide strong positive support for Orton's theory.

Defects of Perceptual Maturation

The results of this study did conform in certain respects to the explanations of specific reading disability tentatively proposed by Birch (1962). The widespread impairment of visual and auditory abilities in conjunction with possibly superior somesthetic abilities in Retarded Readers could be interpreted as a failure to develop visual and auditory dominance in a normal manner following the early dominance of somesthetic sensitivity. Also, the apparently normal development of certain simple habits of visual and auditory functioning in Retarded Readers would fit Birch's suggestion that reading disability is a result of inadequate development of higher levels of visual perception. In general, these suggestions regarding the hierarchical development of perceptual abilities seem more applicable to the pattern of deficit in the Retarded Readers than were the theoretical explanations of Hermann and Orton.

Immaturity of Gestalt Functioning

Although the data of the present studies conform to de Hirsch's (1954) findings that children with reading disability tend to have relatively low Wechsler-Bellevue Verbal IQ, poor auditory memory span, and difficulty with all types of symbols, there seems no particular reason to attribute such deficiencies to a disturbance of Gestalt functioning. In the series of tests of visual perceptual speed, one subtest (Measure 94) required discrimination among figures on the basis of figure-ground relationships. Although the Retarded Readers were significantly deficient on this task (Measure 94), the statistical difference was smaller than that for all but one of the other 12 tests of visual perceptual speed. Thus, the postulation of a Gestalt disturbance, while not unreasonable, does not seem to provide a useful focus for explanation of the pattern of observed deficiency.

Relation of Present Results to Patterns
of Deficit Found in Previous Studies

The extent of nonreading deficit found in the present study and the suggestion that the strengths and weaknesses of Retarded Readers might be explained in terms of defective perceptual maturation seem to fit the description of primary reading retardation proposed by Rabinovitch *et al* (1954). However, the pattern of deficit found in this study did not agree in all details with the pattern described by Rabinovitch *et al*. Several of the deficits associated with primary reading retardation, such as right-left confusion, sensory suppression, mixed dominance, and nonspecific motor incoordination, were not among the more severe nonreading deficiencies of the present group of Retarded Readers. The concept of primary reading retardation, like the concept of a disturbance of Gestalt functioning, was not entirely appropriate to the findings of this study.

The results of the present study also conform in overall scope to the nonreading deficit described by Myklebust and Johnson (1962) for cases classified as childhood dyslexia. In particular, the symptom designated as dyschronometria seems to describe the severe nonreading deficits observed in the present study on the task which required rhyming (Measure 73) and the task which required the sequential naming of months (Measure 70). As before, the pattern of observed deficit in the present study did not correspond in all respects to the symptoms of childhood dyslexia described by Myklebust and Johnson. In a like manner the nonreading deficit found by Silver and Hagin (1960; 1964) corresponded in general scope but not in specific details to the results of the present study.

COMPARISON OF GROUPS WITH LEFT-HANDED SUBJECTS EXCLUDED

There were 5 left-handed boys among Retarded Readers and 7 left-handed boys among Normal Readers. Since the inclusion of these children might tend to prevent the emergence of lateralized deficits, the analysis of covariance was repeated with left-handed subjects eliminated. This analysis revealed no trends toward lateralized deficit in right-handed children. The only changes noted were a reduction below the level of statistical significance of differences between groups in strength of grip with the nonpreferred hand (Measure 55), finger agnosia of the left hand (Measure 46), and spatial orientation (Measure 104). Since the total group of Retarded Readers had been slightly deficient in all 3 skills, the reduction of statistical significance suggests that any possibility of lateralized deficit was restricted to left-handed Retarded Readers. Although the sample of left-handed Retarded Readers was too small for meaningful group comparisons, the individual results of one of the left-handed subjects will be considered in a later chapter.

STATISTICAL COMPARISON OF RETARDED READERS WITH FEMALE NORMAL READERS

The group of 39 Female Normal Readers was equated in reading status with the Male Normal Readers (Table 2, p. 22) and in age and Performance IQ with both Male Normal Readers and Retarded Readers (Table 1, p. 21, and Table 3, p. 23). The statistical comparisons of Retarded Readers and Female Normal Readers by analysis of covariance agreed quite well with the comparisons between Retarded Readers and Male Normal Readers. For 92 of the 109 comparisons the same significant and nonsignificant differences occurred for Female Normal Readers versus Retarded Readers as had occurred for Male Normal Readers versus Retarded Readers. The 17 measures for which different results occurred included 4 in which a significant deficiency in Retarded Readers became nonsignificant, 4 in which a significant superiority of Retarded Readers became nonsignificant, 7 in which a nonsignificant difference became a significant deficiency in Retarded Readers, and 2 in which a nonsignificant difference became a significant superiority in Retarded Readers.

The 4 tests in which significant deficiency in Retarded Readers became nonsignificant when compared with Female Normal Readers included the Wechsler Comprehension subtest (Measure 9), the Halstead Category Test (Measure 21), and grip strength with both hands (Measures 54 and 55). The weaker grip strength of Female Normal Readers probably reflects a predictable sex difference. However, the results for the Comprehension and Category tests are not necessarily attributable to sex difference, and may suggest normal functioning of Retarded Readers for a relatively high-level verbal skill and for an important diagnostic test of brain damage.

On 4 of the 5 measures on which Retarded Readers had been found significantly superior to Male Normal Readers, they did not differ significantly from Female Normal Readers. These included 2 measures from the Tactual Performance Test (Measures 22 and 24) and 2 measures of astereognosis (Measures 49 and 50), all of which involved somesthetic input.

The measures in which the Male Normal and Retarded Readers had not differed significantly, and on which Female Normal Readers were significantly superior to Retarded Readers, included writing speed with both hands (Measures 56 and 57), finger agnosia of the right hand (Measure 45), expression of ideas (Measure 74), and drawings of a house and a wheel (Measures 79 and 81). In addition, they were significantly superior on the only test of visual perceptual speed (Measure 97) on which Retarded Readers had not been deficient in comparison with Male Normal Readers. The 2 tests on which the Retarded Readers became significantly superior to Female Normal Readers were the Picture Completion Test (Measure 15) and visual suppression, left side (Measure 43).

The net shift in significant differences when Female Normal Readers were compared to Retarded Readers was an increase of 3 measures on which Retarded Readers were significantly deficient and a decrease of 2 measures on which Retarded Readers were significantly superior. The major trends, of a combined verbal and visual deficit, remained unchanged. However, the possibility of somesthetic superiority of Retarded Readers was diminished. In a limited way, then, the pattern of deficit in Retarded Readers was partially replicated by comparison with a second group of normal readers, thus reducing the possibility that any significant differences which occurred in both comparisons were the results of chance variations among the sample of normal readers. These results provide a further verification of the extent of nonreading deficit in Retarded Readers, which was the most important finding of the present study.

SUMMARY OF THE RESULTS OF TEST-BY-TEST STATISTICAL COMPARISONS

Test-by-test statistical comparisons of Retarded Readers and Normal Readers revealed that the disability of Retarded Readers was not restricted to skills that required reading or spelling. Rather, the Normal Readers were significantly superior to Retarded Readers on 62 of the 103 measures that were statistically analyzed. The pattern of deficit can best be characterized as an interaction of visual and verbal impairment, involving both verbal and nonverbal visual skills and both visual and auditory verbal skills. There also appeared to be rather selective motor involvement, with definite impairment on several complex drawing tasks and on all tests which required rapid responses to complex visual stimuli. Whether the extensive nonreading deficit was wholly or partially a secondary result of specific reading disability, or whether the severe reading disability of the Retarded Readers was an inevitable consequence of the joint occurrence of poor aptitude for certain visual and verbal skills, cannot be entirely determined within the scope of the present study. The interpretation of results was somewhat complicated by the irregular performance of Retarded Readers on the set of tasks which served as the criterion of normal nonverbal intelligence.

The results of test-by-test statistical analysis were also interpreted by comparing the pattern of deficit among Retarded Readers in this study to the configurations of impairment observed in adults with brain damage, to the causal factors postulated by several theoretical explanations of reading disability, and to the characteristics of retarded readers found in previous studies of specific reading disability. The configuration of impairment of the Retarded Readers on tests from the Indiana Neuropsychology Battery did not correspond closely to the types of impairment seen in adult patients with brain damage having either lateralized or nonlateralized lesions. The results for the Minnesota Aphasia Test showed a relative subtle disturbance of visual and verbal abilities in Retarded Readers similar to that found in aphasic adults with visual involvement. Of the various theoretical explanations of reading disability, the results of this study did not strongly support theories which postulated right-left disorientation, incomplete cerebral dominance, or immaturity of Gestalt functioning as causes of specific reading disability. The occurrence of deficiencies of complex visual and auditory skills in conjunction with a possible superiority of Retarded Readers in certain somesthetic skills did, however, conform to explanations of reading disability in terms of defective perceptual maturation. The impairment of nonreading skills which occurred among Retarded Readers in this study agreed quite well with descriptions proposed by other investigators of specific reading disability with regard to the extent of nonreading impairment, but did not agree in all specific features of observed deficit.

The development history, neurological status, and overall adjustment of Retarded Readers and Normal Readers are considered in the next chapter. Following this, the results of further analyses of individual and grouped test results are presented in an attempt to broaden the perspective for interpreting the nonreading deficiencies of Retarded Readers.

CHAPTER SIX

Neurological Status, Developmental History, and Family History of Reading Problems

(IN COLLABORATION WITH ARTHUR L. DREW)

The neurological and case-history findings presented in this chapter were obtained for the purpose of determining whether any significant factors of inheritance, birth and development, accident and illness, or neurological deficiency were associated with reading disability in the present group of retarded readers. The current neurological status of almost all of the Retarded Readers and over half of the Normal Readers was assessed by a brief neurological examination; and a developmental history and a history of family reading problems were obtained for almost all subjects by completion of the forms shown in Appendix B (p. 165) during an interview with a parent. It must be noted again that the case-history information was based upon a retrospective, subjective interview; and that this information cannot be considered comparable in validity to the other data of this study.

QUANTITATIVE ESTIMATE OF NEUROLOGICAL STATUS

A quantitative estimate of the probability of neurological dysfunction was made by a neurologist (A. L. Drew) for the 35 Retarded Readers, 22 Male Normal Readers, and 21 Female Normal Readers on whom complete neurological and interview information had been obtained. For each child there were 2 separate ratings, with the first based upon an evaluation of the written report of the neurological examination only, and the second based upon a joint evaluation of the neurological report and the case history reports. In each instance a numerical rating of the probability of neurological involvement was assigned according to the following scale:

0 — normal
1 — probably normal
2 — definite but minimum involvement) "soft signs"
3 — definite abnormality)
4 — probably pathological) pathological diagnosis
5 — definitely pathological)

The neurological reports alone and the reports combined with case history reports were given to the neurologist in random order, with no overt identification of name or reading status. For the judgments

TABLE 9

Rated probability of neurological involvement among Normal Readers and Retarded Readers, with the number of children in each category indicated.

Rating	Retarded Readers (N = 35)	Male Normal Readers (N = 22)	Female Normal Readers (N = 21)
1. Rating based upon report of neurological examination only:			
0 normal	6	16	13
1 probably normal	3	3	4
2 definite but minimum involvement	6	2	4
3 definite abnormality	8	0	0
4 probably pathological	11	1	0
5 definitely pathological	1	0	0
2. Rating based upon both neurological report and case history information:			
0 normal	20	17	17
1 probably normal	4	3	2
2 definite but minimum involvement	7	1	1
3 definite abnormality	2	1	1
4 probably pathological	1	0	0
5 definitely pathological	1	0	0

based upon neurological status alone, which were made first, there was no indication of reading status. However, reading status could be inferred from several items in the case history forms, which meant that the ratings based upon both neurological and case history information could not be made without some knowledge regarding reading status. Also, as mentioned previously, the influence of examiner bias during the neurological examination could not be evaluated.

Table 9 shows the distribution of ratings for each group. Where the rating was based only upon the result of the neurological examination the rated probability of neurological involvement was much higher among Retarded Readers, with only 9 of 35 Retarded Readers receiving a normal rating, as compared with 19 of 22 Male Normal Readers and 17 of 21 Female Normal Readers. The proportion of Retarded Readers judged to be not normal neurologically (rating of 2 or above) was significantly higher (p. < .001) than the proportions of Male Normal Readers and Female Normal Readers judged to be not normal neurologically.

When the rating was based upon both the neurological report and the case history information, many more of the Retarded Readers were judged to be within normal neurological limits, and the differences between groups were not statistically significant. Thus, about two thirds of the Retarded Readers were rated as neurologically normal when the judgment was based upon a neurological examination plus case history, whereas only about one fourth were rated as normal on the basis of the neurological report alone. In contrast, over four fifths of the Normal Readers were judged normal by both procedures.

The higher incidence of judged neurological abnormality among Retarded Readers under the first rating system resulted from the larger number of specific neurological signs noted during the examination of Retarded Readers, as will be seen in the following section. The number of pathological ratings was reduced when the judgments included case history information, because in some instances the information in the case history failed to provide necessary augmenting evidence of neurological impairment, and in other instances the case history provided extenuating reasons for the occurrence of neurological signs. These quantitative assessments of neurological status demonstrated that Retarded Readers were more likely to show overt signs of neurological deficit, but that these signs were of doubtful significance in suggesting serious underlying neuropathology.

DETAILED RESULTS OF NEUROLOGICAL EXAMINATIONS

All neurological examinations were carried out by resident physicians of the Department of Neurology, Indiana University Medical Center. Of the 35 Retarded Readers who were examined, 24 were examined by one Resident (Dr. Caridad Cruz), 10 by a second Resident (Dr. Peter P. Morgan), and 1 by a third Resident (Dr. Harold L. Booker). All 43 of the Normal Readers were examined by Dr. Cruz.

Of the specific neurological signs noted during the neurological examinations, the most common among Retarded Readers was right-left confusion, with 23 of the 35 Retarded Readers judged to have some degree of right-left confusion, in comparison with only one Male Normal Reader and 2 Female Normal Readers. Other common neurological signs noted in Retarded Readers were active but equal muscle stretch reflexes in lower extremities in 6 cases, decreased swing of right arm on walking (3 cases), finger agnosia (3), muscle stretch reflexes active but equal in all extremities (2), "mirror" movement of foot with hand movement (2), right Babinski (2), lower right shoulder position while walking (2), and inability to name fingers (2). There was one case each of the following observed signs in Retarded Readers: extensor toe signs, left; diminished superficial abdominal reflexes on the left; impaired position sense, right toes; muscle power of right hand less than left; café au lait spot on right leg; left ear thinner than right; tongue movements around lips; strong jaw jerk; slightly larger right palpebral fissure; left side of the frontal region flattened; suggestion of mild right central facial palsy; poor number writing identification on palms bilaterally; many facial mannerisms; equivocal Babinski, right arm drift; very mild hemiatrophy of left side of face and forehead; suppressed hand on both sides in simultaneous cheek-hand stimulation; left sternocleidomastoid weaker; left ear lower; right hand and fingers and foot and toes shorter than left; bilateral astereognosis; dysadiokokinesis bilaterally; ear lobules not well formed; deep tendon reflexes on left greater than right; pronounced Mayer's sign on left; and left knee and ankle jerk much greater than right.

Fewer specific signs were noted for Normal Readers. For the 22 Male Normal Readers there was one instance each of the following observed signs: associated right arm swing; lower position of right arm when walking; less deep naso-labial fold on the right when smiling; muscle stretch reflexes hyperactive but symmetrical; café au lait spots on right ankle, left arm, right forearm; mild right-left confusion; syndactyly of second and third toes bilaterally, nystagmus bilaterally on lateral gaze; inability to name fingers; and inability to recognize coins on either hand. Among the 21 Female Normal Readers there were 2 instances of mild right-left confusion and 2 reports of inability to recognize coins in either hand; and one instance each of right shoulder lower and less associated arm swing on the right when walking, partial syndactyly of second and third toes bilaterally, several mistakes on number writing on the left palm, and inability to name fingers.

Aside from the much greater incidence of right-left confusion in Retarded Readers, the difference between groups in neurological symptomatology appeared to be quantitative rather than qualitative. Although the incidence of neurological signs was much higher among Retarded Readers, a number of specific symptoms were common to all 3 groups. The report of right-left confusion in two thirds of the Retarded Readers was the one feature which sharply distinguished Retarded from Normal Readers. This provided a much stronger indication of directional confusion than was shown in the test of directional confusion (Measure 104), in which there was a great deal of overlap in error scores between Retarded and Normal Readers.

DEVELOPMENTAL HISTORY
AND FAMILY BACKGROUND

The standard interview forms were intended to provide systematic information regarding possible differences between Normal and Retarded Readers in complications of pregnancy and delivery, disorders of infancy and childhood, current health status, and family history of reading problems. About 150 items of information were obtained by completing the forms shown in Appendix B (p. 165). As implied by the ratings shown in Table 9 (p. 71), the groups were not sharply differentiated by case history information. In the following sections the most pertinent parts of the interview information are summarized for the children on whom complete information was obtained. This included 37 of the 39 Retarded Readers and 38 of 39 Male Normal Readers. Female Normal Readers were not included in this part of the analysis. It should be noted that in addition to the general unreliability of information obtained by a retrospective procedure, the interviews were not conducted by physicians. In many cases questionable descriptions of symptoms and disease were recorded verbatim which could have been clarified by further questioning if the interview had been conducted by a physician.

Pregnancy and Delivery

Pregnancy Complications. The groups did not differ greatly in the incidence and general severity of pregnancy complications. Among the mothers of the 37 Retarded Readers there were 27 uncomplicated pregnancies, 2 with emotional stress during pregnancy, 2 with bleeding during term, and one each reporting high blood pressure with uremic poisoning, bronchial asthma and general difficulty, a fall at 7 months, sickness and vomiting during entire term, a near miscarriage at 7 months attributed to Rh Factor, and constant sickness with a fall at 7 months. Among the mothers of the 38 Normal Readers there were 28 uncomplicated pregnancies, 2 with a "heart condition" during pregnancy, and one each with bleeding, a fall during pregnancy, hospitalization with an unspecified infection during seventh month, edema and excessive weight gain, high blood pressure with constant sickness and several convulsions, edema, anemia and low blood pressure, and high blood pressure with gall bladder trouble.

Delivery. Thirty of the Retarded Readers were born in normal term, with one seven-month, 5 eight-month, and one ten-month term; 36 of the Normal Readers were normal term deliveries, and for the remaining 2 the delivery term was 8 months. In estimated duration of labor there was a higher proportion of both short and long labor times among the Retarded Readers, as follows:

Estimated Duration of Labor (hours)	Retarded Readers	Normal Readers
less than 3	8	3
3–6	14	22
7–10	4	7
11–24	6	6
25–48	1	0
over 48	3	0
"long"	1	0

The durations in the 3 cases of more than 48 hours labor in the Retarded Reader group were $2\frac{1}{2}$, 4, and 5 days. The groups did not differ greatly in type of delivery, 29 Retarded Readers were normal births, with one each reported as breech birth, Caesarean section, instrumental delivery, dry birth, posterior birth, induced but otherwise normal, held back but otherwise normal, and breech with instruments; 29 Normal Readers were normal births; 4 involved the use of instruments, 2 were breech births, and one each were reported as Caesarean section, dry birth, and held back.

Condition at birth. The Retarded Readers tended to weigh less at birth than Normal Readers, as follows:

Birth Weight (lbs.)	Retarded Readers	Normal Readers
4-5	2	0
5-6	8	0
6-8	17	21
8-10	6	15
10-12	1	2
"normal"	2	0
unknown	1	0

Information regarding length at birth was much less complete, especially among Retarded Readers. The available data indicated no marked differences between groups:

Length at Birth (in.)	Retarded Readers	Normal Readers
15-17	2	1
18-19	4	6
20-22	7	24
"normal"	1	3
unknown	23	4

The majority of children in both groups were reported to be in good condition at birth, including 31 Retarded Readers and 33 Normal Readers. Among the remaining 6 Retarded Readers, one had a cleft palate (corrected at age 2), another was an Rh baby, and the others included pyloric stenosis, an appearance of lethargy (to mother), some jaundice, and head scratched from instrument delivery. The 5 remaining Normal Readers included 2 children bruised from instruments and one case each of difficulty in breathing, broken nose, and deformed foot coupled with viral pneumonia.

Early Development

Neonatal. Only 5 of the Retarded Readers required an incubator, for periods of one week, 10 days, 2 weeks, 3 weeks, and 7 weeks; and only one of the Normal Readers was placed in an incubator, for a period of 2 days. For 30 of the Retarded Readers there were no problems associated with feeding. Among the 7 children for whom problems were reported, there were 2 cases of difficulty in bowel movement and one case each of colic of 6 weeks duration, a digestive problem which required use of lactic acid, an unspecified digestive problem of 2 weeks, a child who "couldn't hold down" food for the first month, and digestive difficulty associated with pyloric stenosis. All but 3 of the 38 Normal Readers had no feeding problems. These 3 cases included

TABLE 10

Ages at which various developmental stages were achieved by 37 Retarded Readers (RR) and 38 Male Normal Readers (NR), with the number of children in each category indicated.

Nearest Age	Holding up Head		Sitting		Crawling		Walking		Talking		Toilet Training	
	RR	NR	RR	NR	RR	NR	RR	NR	RR	NR	RR	NR
3 months	31	31		3								
6 months	1	1	29	31	1	10			2	5		
9 months				1	27	18	8	12	3	21		
1 year							25	24	7	9	2	7
18 months							3	2	1	2	1	12
2 years											5	15
3 years									2		2	1
4 years									1			1
over 4 "normal"							1		20		27	2
"late" or "slow"	3		2		3				1			
unknown	2	6	6	3	6	10				1		

colic of a year's duration, feeding difficulty associated with asthma, and feeding difficulty associated with viral pneumonia.

Infancy and early childhood. Estimates of the various stages of development are notoriously susceptible to inadequate definition and imperfect recall. With these shortcomings in mind, the reports regarding several developmental stages are summarized in Table 10. With the exception of 4 of the Retarded Readers the groups did not differ in the reported age distribution for holding up the head, sitting, and crawling. The total of eight reports of "late" or "slow" achievement for holding up head, sitting, and crawling was attributed to 4 of the Retarded Readers, one of whom was reported slow in all 3 stages. The group distributions for age of walking were essentially identical. Discrepancies in the reports for talking and toilet training were attributable to slight differences of interview methods and to the ambiguity of defining these developmental phenomena. The majority of Retarded Readers were reportedly normal in achieving both stages. There were, however, 3 Retarded Readers reported slower in talking than any of the Normal Readers. Although there was no discernable difference between groups in age of toilet training, enuresis to age 5 or beyond was reported for 10 Retarded Readers and for only 4 Normal Readers.

Illnesses and diseases of childhood. A history of childhood illnesses and diseases was obtained by asking the parent to recall these. It is almost certain that a different incidence would have been obtained if a standard checklist had been used. The following disorders were reported:

Disease	Retarded Readers	Normal Readers
Measles	37	36
Chickenpox	35	32
Mumps	27	29
Whooping Cough	5	2
Scarlet fever (scarlatina)	6	14
Diphtheria	0	0
Meningitis	0	0
Polio	0	0
Tonsillitis	6	11
Bronchitis	2	2
Pneumonia	2	3
Appendicitis	1	1
Rheumatic fever	1	0
Throat infection	4	2
Ear infection	2	0
Kidney infection	0	1
Sinus infection	1	0
Lymph infection	0	1
Other infection	0	3
Allergies	2	1
Chronic nosebleed	1	0
Chronic headache	1	0
Chronic stomach ache	1	0
Epilepsy	0	0

Fevers and convulsions. At least one occurrence of a fever of 103° or more was reported for 12 of the Retarded Readers and 22 of the Normal Readers. A series of convulsions preceding bowel movements at the age of 5 months was reported for one Retarded Reader, and a single convulsion during an attack of pneumonia was reported for one Normal Reader and one Retarded Reader.

Injuries and loss of consciousness. Cuts severe enough to require stitches were reported for 7 Retarded Readers and 8 Normal Readers; broken bones (including broken noses) were reported for 5 Retarded Readers and 8 Normal Readers. Loss of consciousness was much more common among Normal Readers, with 3 children who had fainted at least once, 5 who had been knocked unconscious at least once, one overcome by gas, and one who became unconscious "when given too strong a medicine"; among Retarded Readers 3 had fainted at least once, and 3 had been knocked unconscious once. There were also reports of relatively severe blows to the head which did not produce unconsciousness in 4 Retarded Readers and 3 Normal Readers.

Operations. The most common operation reported was tonsillectomy-adenoidectomy. The remaining operations reported were confined largely to Retarded Readers, as follows:

Operational Procedures	Retarded Readers	Normal Readers
Tonsillectomy-adenoidectomy	16	10
Appendectomy	1	1
Hernia Correction	1	1
Cleft Palate correction	1	
Strabismus correction	2	
Deviated septum correction		1
Clipping of lingual frenum	1	
Removal of nasal polyps	1	
Lymph gland removal	1	
Ear abscess removal	1	
Removal of small tumor of hip		1
Spinal tap	2	
Blood transfusion	2	

Coordination problems. A specific inquiry was made as to problems of motor coordination. None were reported for Normal Readers. Among Retarded Readers only 2 instances of coordination difficulty were reported: one child was said to have been slow but eventually successful in learning to ride a bicycle; and a second child required 2 months to learn to ride a bicycle at age 11.

Other difficulties. The parent was also asked to report any difficulties of growth and development that had not been mentioned in response to previous inquiries. Such additional difficulties were reported for 4 of the Retarded Readers, with the following complaints: falling asleep in class; playing for hours with clay and very small toys; easily excited, going into hysterics during thunderstorms; and very sensitive and easily upset by family difficulties. There were also 4 normal children in whom additional difficulties were reported, including stuttering from ages 4 to 8, a discipline problem in the home situation, a severe dental problem, and a difficulty in blood coagulation.

Siblings. The 2 groups did not differ systematically in number of siblings, as the following distribution shows:

Number of Siblings	Retarded Readers	Normal Readers
0	2	5
1	10	8
2	11	12
3	8	5
4	5	4
5 or more	1	4

Complications of pregnancy were reported for siblings in the families of 5 Retarded Readers and 5 Normal Readers. Developmental complications were reported for siblings in the families of 12 Retarded Readers and 8 Normal Readers.

Educational History

All of the Retarded Readers had severe difficulty in educational achievement, and tended to obtain low or failing grades in the majority of subjects; the Normal Readers tended to be average in educational achievement. All but one of the Retarded Readers were enrolled in regular classes.

Age of beginning primary education. Seventeen of the Retarded Readers and 4 of the Normal Readers had attended kindergarten. Two Retarded Readers and 7 Normal Readers began Grade 1 at age 5, the remaining 35 Retarded Readers and 31 Normal Readers began Grade 1 at age 6.

Number of grades repeated. Only 4 of the Retarded Readers had not repeated a grade, 24 had repeated one grade, 6 had repeated 2 grades, and 3 had repeated more than 2 grades. Only one Normal Reader had repeated one-half grade, and the remainder had not repeated any grades. Of the 4 Retarded Readers who had not repeated a grade, 2 were passed despite poor grades, one was not graded by the usual system because of his reading difficulty, and in the final case it was reported that the child had obtained good grades until the year prior to testing.

General Status at Time of Testing

Information was obtained from the parent regarding the current status of vision, speech, hearing, and adjustment in the home and school situation.

Vision. Among Retarded Readers there were 2 cases of corrected myopia, one corrected astigmatism and myopia, one muscular weakness, and one muscular weakness with corrected myopia. Among Normal Readers there were 9 cases of corrected myopia and one color blindness.

Hearing. No current hearing problems were reported for Normal Readers; in the only report of a hearing problem among Retarded Readers the mother mentioned a possible difficulty in understanding speech that was presumably the sequel of a concussion at age 10.

Speech. Mild articulation disorders were reported for 3 Retarded Readers; no current speech disorders were reported for Normal Readers.

Eating, sleeping, and self care. No severe eating problems were reported. There was one instance of overeating and 5 of undereating among Retarded Readers, as compared with one case of overeating and 2 of undereating among Normal Readers. Many more sleeping problems were reported for Retarded Readers, including 3 instances of too little sleep, one of too much sleep, 2 of talking during sleep, 2 of bad dreams, 2 of restlessness, and one of light sleeping. For Normal Readers there was one case of too little sleep, and one case of talking during sleep and bad dreams. There were no complaints of difficulty in self care for Normal Readers. Among Retarded Readers one was said to resist bathing and changing clothes, another was totally unconcerned about his personal appearance, and a third presented general difficulty in self care.

Recreational activities. The range of recreational activities of Retarded Readers was quite comparable to that of Normal Readers. The majority of children in both groups participated in sports, watched television regularly, and built model cars or planes. A somewhat larger proportion of Retarded Readers were reportedly active in carpentry, electrical and mechanical work, music, and art. Several children in each group drove motor scooters and motorized go-carts. One of the most severely Retarded Readers was very proficient in racing a junior sports car at speeds up to 50 miles per hour. The one marked difference between groups was in reading. Reading for recreation was reported for 14 of the Normal Readers and none of the Retarded Readers.

Household chores. Fourteen of the 37 Retarded Readers and none of the Normal Readers were said to be not sufficiently helpful in household tasks.

Adjustment to peers. Seven of the Retarded Readers and only one of the Normal Readers were rated as having fair or poor relationships with their peers.

Adjustment in home situation. Both groups were relatively well-adjusted in the home situation. Among Retarded Readers, 5 had difficulty with siblings and 3 had difficulty with parents. Among Normal Readers one came from a broken home.

Adjustment to reading problem. This information was obtained only for Retarded Readers. In 13 cases it was reported that the reading problem did not affect the child's adjustment in the school situation. In 3 cases the child tended to play with younger children because he had been held back in school. Two children were said to have feelings of inferiority. Six children were teased by their schoolmates about poor reading. Three were teased by siblings about poor reading. Four did not like to go to school because of poor reading. And 6 were self-conscious about their reading difficulty.

Family Characteristics

Certain family characteristics of possible relevance to reading problems were investigated, including handedness within the immediate family, parents' education, parents' reading status, incidence of reading problems in the family, and other family difficulties.

Handedness. The groups were very similar with regard to familial incidence of left handedness and ambidexterity. Among the 5 left-handed Retarded Readers, one had an ambidextrous parent, another had a left-handed parent and the remaining 3 had otherwise right-handed families. Among the 32 right-handed Retarded Readers, 20 had entirely right-handed families, 11 families had one ambidextrous or left-handed member, and one family had more than one ambidextrous or left-handed member. Among the 7 left-handed Normal Readers, 5 had otherwise right-handed families, one had a left-handed parent, and another had a left-handed sibling. Among the 31 right-handed Normal Readers, 19 had entirely right-handed families, 11 families had one ambidextrous or left-handed member, and one family had more than one ambidextrous or left-handed member.

Education of parents. The groups were very similar in parental education. In both groups there were 3 families in which one parent had less than an eighth-grade education. Among Retarded Readers there were 3 families in which one parent had education beyond high school and two families in which both parents had education beyond high school; among Normal Readers there were 3 families in which one parent had education beyond high school and two families in which both parents had education beyond high school. For the remaining 29 Retarded Readers and 28 Normal Readers both parents had between 8 and 12 years of education.

Reading status of parents. Despite the similarity in education there was a higher incidence of reading difficulty among parents of Retarded Readers. Three of the mothers of Retarded Readers reported difficulty in learning to read, and one reported difficulty in reading accompanied by a general school problem and a speech problem. Among fathers of Retarded Readers 9 were generally poor in reading and spelling, 2 had general school difficulty, and one had a speech problem in addition to reading difficulty. In at least 2 cases there was a strong indication that the reading problem of the father could have been classified as specific reading disability, and a somewhat weaker suggestion of specific reading disability in 3 other fathers. Among the parents of Normal Readers the only reading problems reported were 2 mothers who did not like to read and one father who was said to be a slow reader.

Other reading problems in family. The determination of other reading problems in the family was complicated by the incomplete knowledge of the person interviewed, especially where members of the spouse's family were concerned, and by the virtual impossibility of differentiating specific reading problems from more general intellectual disorders and school difficulties of family members. Among the 37 Retarded Readers there were 8 families in which no other reading problems were reported. It will be recalled that there were 4 pairs of brothers in the group of Retarded Readers. For one of these pairs there were no additional family reading problems; the father of a second pair and the mother of a third pair had reading difficulty; and general school difficulty was reported for the sister, the mother's uncle's child, and the father's cousin's child of the fourth pair. Among the 21 remaining Retarded Readers there were 8 families with one additional reading problem, including a brother in 4 instances, a father in 2 instances, a mother's brother, and a mother's sister's son. The 8 instances of 2 additional reading problems included 2 brothers, brother and sister, father and brother, mother and brother, brother and maternal uncle, sister and maternal uncle, father and paternal uncle, and maternal niece and male second cousin. The remaining 5 families of Retarded Readers contained more than 2 additional problem readers, as follows:

> father, paternal siblings, maternal aunt
> father, paternal uncle, paternal niece
> father, maternal grandfather, maternal uncle
> father, brother, sister
> father, mother, brother, paternal uncle and three
> aunts, paternal niece

The incidence of reading problems was much lower in the families of Normal Readers. No reading problems were reported in the families of 26 of the 38 children. There were 7 families with one reading problem, including the 2 mothers who did not like to read, 3 cases in which a brother had reading difficulty, a maternal cousin, and a paternal uncle. The remaining 5 families had the following multiple reading problems:

> maternal brother and maternal cousin
> father and paternal brother
> maternal brother and two maternal nephews
> sister, maternal brother, maternal niece
> two brothers and a sister, a maternal niece and nephew

SUMMARY OF NEUROLOGICAL AND CASE HISTORY FINDINGS

When the probability of neurological dysfunction was estimated from the neurological examination alone, a significantly higher proportion of Retarded Readers were judged to be neurologically abnormal. When the estimate was based upon both the neurological and case history information, however, the Retarded Reader group did not differ significantly from the groups of Male and Female Normal Readers.

The incidence of specific neurological and case history findings for Retarded Readers and Male Normal Readers was examined in some detail. The one specific symptom which occurred with much higher frequency among Retarded Readers was right-left disorientation. Otherwise, although the total number of additional symptoms was greater for Retarded Readers, there were no noteworthy differences in the pattern of symptomatology.

Case history findings showed no difference between groups in some aspects, and mild or marked deficiencies were evident in the Retarded Readers in other aspects of developmental history and family background. Although the groups did not differ in complications of pregnancy, type of delivery, and general condition at birth, there was a somewhat higher incidence of prematurity, short and long labor, and low birth weight in Retarded Readers. The incidence of early feeding problems and the necessity of incubators was also slightly higher in Retarded Readers.

With the exception of a small subset of 4 Retarded Readers, the groups did not differ in reported age of holding up the head, sitting, crawling, and walking. The groups did not differ in toilet training except for a slightly higher incidence of continued enuresis among Retarded Readers. And except for 3 slow talkers among Retarded Readers the groups did not differ in reported age of talking.

The groups did not differ systematically in illness, diseases of childhood, general injuries, head injuries, loss of consciousness, or other pathology, except for a slightly higher incidence of operations among Retarded Readers. There were 2 cases of reported coordination difficulty among Retarded Readers.

The groups did not differ in age of entering school, but Retarded Readers were inferior in all reported aspects of educational achievement. At the time of testing the groups did not differ in vision or hearing problems. There were several mild articulation problems among Retarded Readers, as well as a higher incidence of sleeping problems, difficulty in relationships with peers, and difficulty in the home situation. About two thirds of the Retarded Readers were said to exhibit some overt difficulty in adjusting to their reading difficulty. However, the range of extracurricular activities of Retarded Readers was remarkably similar to that of Normal Readers, with the only real difference being an absence of recreational reading.

The families of Retarded and Normal Readers did not differ in the distribution of handedness, and the parents of Retarded and Normal Readers did not differ in years of education. However, the incidence of reported reading problems among parents of Retarded Readers was about 40 percent, as compared with fewer than 10 percent among the parents of Normal Readers. And there were, likewise, over three times as many families of Retarded Readers in which one or more individuals, usually males, reported reading problems. The proportion of such cases in which reading retardation was merely one aspect of general intellectual deficiency could not be determined.

The neurological and case history information suggested no clear-cut predisposing conditions for specific reading disability. A number of possibly relevant conditions occurred with greater frequency in Retarded Readers, but there were very few instances in which the frequency of any such condition approached even 50 percent in the Retarded Reader group. Despite the severe and widespread deficiency of Retarded Readers in both reading and nonreading skills, there is nothing in the medical or developmental history of these children which markedly differentiates them from Normal Readers. Moreover, there seems to be nothing that sets these children apart from their normally reading peers in their overall adjustment at home and at school and in the scope of their extracurricular interests and activities. What precise effect such reading and nonreading deficiencies have on the later acquisition of adequate vocational skills is a question worthy of study. In a recent investigation (Carter, 1964) it was found that retarded readers tended to enter unskilled and semi-skilled jobs, and that promotion to higher-level jobs was impeded by the lack of necessary reading skills.

Because of the inherent limitations of the case history interview, the conclusions drawn regarding the medical history, educational history, and life adjustment of the Retarded Readers must be regarded as tentative. Future investigators would be well-advised to formulate more scientifically rigorous procedures for obtaining case history information.

CHAPTER SEVEN

Estimation of the Probability of Cerebral Dysfunction by Analysis of Nonreading Impairment in Individual Subjects

(IN COLLABORATION WITH RALPH M. REITAN AND HALLGRIM KLØVE)

The deficiencies of reading and nonreading skills in Retarded Readers, as revealed by the test-by-test comparison of groups reported in Chapter 6, did not markedly resemble the patterns of impairment which result from lateralized and nonlateralized cerebral lesions in adults. This did not necessarily mean, however, that such patterns of impairment had not occurred in individual subjects. Specific reading disability, as defined in this study, could conceivably result from several different kinds of cerebral dysfunction, whose differential effects might be concealed by group averages.

Although the primary purpose of the present study was to investigate group trends in Retarded Readers, the possible importance of individual differences within the group of Retarded Readers was assessed in 2 ways. The results of a detailed examination of the test profiles of 9 Retarded Readers are presented in Chapter 10. The other procedure of individual analysis involved a further attempt to assess the probability of cerebral dysfunction in Retarded Readers. This procedure is described in the present chapter.

As part of a continuing research program at the Indiana University Neuropsychology Laboratory, methods have been developed for estimating the location, extent, and type of cerebral lesions in individual patients from results of a standard battery of tests administered by trained technicians who have no knowledge of the patient's neurological status (Reitan, 1959, 1965). The estimate of cerebral dysfunction is derived from a "blind" interpretation of the test results by one of the psychologists in the laboratory, without knowledge of the patient's history or neurological status. This interpretation is later compared with a complete summary of neurological and neurosurgical findings for the patient. A remarkably high accuracy of estimation has been achieved by repeated application and revision of these predictive procedures during more than a decade of research in the Neuropsychology Laboratory. The successful development of a method for making precise estimates of brain lesions solely on the basis of psychological test scores has obvious implications for increased understanding of the brain-behavior relationship.

Most of the tests used in the Neuropsychology Laboratory for estimation of brain lesions were administered in the present study. It was decided that estimation of the probability of cerebral dysfunction in individual children by the method described above would provide an extremely valuable adjunct to the statistical analyses of group trends. A special procedure was devised for "blind" evaluation of the 39 Retarded Readers and 39 Male Normal Readers whereby all information giving a direct indication of reading status was removed from the test results, and the estimate of brain function was made by assigning the subject to one of a limited set of predictive categories.

The estimates of cerebral dysfunction were made by the two psychologists (R. M. Reitan and H. Kløve) who had developed the interpretive method used in the Indiana Neuropsychology Laboratory. Although both judges were familiar with the purposes and procedures of this study, neither was aware of the exact composition of the samples of Normal and Retarded Readers.

The 78 records of individual test results were arranged in a random sequence and independently evaluated by the 2 judges. The only identifying information on each record was a code number, plus the child's age, sex, and handedness. All test scores for tasks which required reading or spelling had been eliminated. These included reading and spelling achievement scores (Measures 1 and 2), the written form of the Peabody Picture Vocabulary Test (Measure 35), the Halstead Speech Perception Test (Measure 28), and all reading, writing, and spelling items from the Halstead-Wepman Aphasia Screening Test.

The following tests were included on the standard record forms used for estimates of cerebral dysfunction:

> Wechsler-Bellevue Intelligence Scale (Measures 3-18)
> Trail Making Test (Measures 19 and 20)
> Halstead Category Test (Measure 21)
> Halstead Tactual Performance Test (Measures 22-26)
> Seashore Rhythm Test (Measure 27)
> Halstead Tapping Test (Measures 29, 30)
> Halstead Time Sense Test (Measures 31, 32)
> Lateral Dominance Examination (Measures 51-57)
> Halstead-Wepman Aphasia Screening Test (Measures 36-39 plus
>   unnumbered items), excluding items requiring reading,
>   writing, and spelling
> Tests of Sensory and Perceptual Disturbances (Measures 41-50)

The results of the Neuropsychology Tests are usually interpreted by a discussion of the kinds of brain lesion which could have led to the test findings under consideration, followed by a specific prediction of the locus, extent, and type of lesion (Reitan, 1959, 1965), but the judgments required in this study were restricted to a small number of predetermined categories. The judge was first asked to classify a given set of test results into one of the following probabilistic categories: no cerebral dysfunction, minimal cerebral dysfunction, or definite cerebral dysfunction. The second category, minimal cerebral dysfunction, was used when the judge did not feel that actual brain damage was present, but still did not consider the test results to be perfectly normal. Where a judgment of minimal or definite cerebral dysfunction was made, a further estimate of probable location and extent (diffuse, right hemisphere, right hemisphere diffuse, left hemisphere, or left hemisphere diffuse) was required. The specific rules used for assigning these ratings were formulated in advance by the 2 judges (see Appendix D).

Several additional differences between the ratings used in the present study and the usual estimates of cerebral dysfunction in the Neuropsychology Laboratory should be noted. The exclusion of scores indicative of reading status reduced the amount of information available to the judge, especially information regarding verbal abilities, which might be differentially affected by lateralized lesions. The predictive procedures had largely been developed from examination of the test results of adult patients, and the judges' previous experience with children in the age range of the present study had often been hampered by a lack of clear neurological findings. Finally, the context in which judgments were to be made was quite a different one, since it was assumed that the majority of patients tested in the Laboratory had been referred through a physician, whereas almost all of the children in the present study had been obtained directly from the community.

RESULTS OF INDIVIDUAL EVALUATIONS

Because of the limited number of categories in which judgments were made, it was possible to indicate the exact amount of agreement between the 2 psychologists, who are designated as Judge A and Judge B. Table 11 shows the estimates of no cerebral dysfunction, minimal cerebral dysfunction, and definite cerebral dysfunction. The results for each group are listed separately, with the estimates of Judge A given in the bottom row, the estimates of Judge B given in the right-hand column, and the degree of correspondence between these estimates indicated in the body of each table.

Both judges made more ratings of no cerebral dysfunction in the Normal Reader group and more ratings of definite cerebral dysfunction in the Retarded Reader group. When these 2 categories are considered separately, the tendencies to rate the Normal Readers as having no cerebral dysfunction and the Retarded Readers as having definite cerebral dysfunction are much more obvious:

		None	Definite
Judge A	Retarded Readers	3	13
	Normal Readers	14	3
Judge B	Retarded Readers	5	20
	Normal Readers	12	9

This trend was statistically significant for both judges as demonstrated by Chi-Square tests (df = 1, corrected for continuity) significant beyond the .01 level for Judge A and beyond the .05 level for Judge B.

TABLE 11

Estimates of the probability of cerebral dysfunction obtained from "blind" interpretations of the Neuropsychology test results of individual subjects, with all
scores indicative of reading status excluded. The ratings of Judge A are given at
the bottom of each table and ratings by Judge B at the right side of each table, with
correspondence between the Judges' ratings indicated in the body of each table.

1. Retarded Readers (N = 39)

	None	Minimal	Definite		
No cerebral dysfunction	3	2	0	5	Judge B
Minimal cerebral dysfunction	0	10	4	14	
Definite cerebral dysfunction	0	11	9	20	
	3	23	13		

Judge A

2. Normal Readers (N = 39)

	None	Minimal	Definite		
No cerebral dysfunction	8	4	0	12	Judge B
Minimal cerebral dysfunction	6	12	0	18	
Definite cerebral dysfunction	0	6	3	9	
	14	22	3		

Judge A

The agreement between judges was quite good. There was no case
of complete disagreement — i.e., in which one judge estimated no cerebral dysfunction and the other estimated definite cerebral dysfunction.
The major differences were produced by the tendency of Judge B to
make more ratings of definite cerebral dysfunction for both groups.
The degree of overlap between Normal Readers and Retarded Readers
is indicated by the number of judgments of minimal cerebral dysfunction made by both judges for both groups. Both judges, then, agreed in
assigning a higher proportion of ratings of definite cerebral dysfunction
to the Retarded Reader group and a higher proportion of no cerebral
dysfunction ratings to Normal Readers, with a considerable number of
minimal cerebral dysfunction ratings made by both judges for both
groups.

The estimates of the 2 judges were next pooled by a simple summation procedure, with a value of 0 assigned to a judgment of no cerebral dysfunction, 1 to minimum cerebral dysfunction, and 2 to definite
cerebral dysfunction. By this method, a child rated by both judges as
having no cerebral dysfunction would have a total rating of 0, and a
child rated by both judges as having definite cerebral dysfunction would
receive a total rating of 4. The following distributions of pooled ratings
were obtained:

Pooled Ratings of Probable Cerebral Dysfunction

	0	1	2	3	4
Retarded Readers	3	2	10	15	9
Normal Readers	8	10	12	6	3

This tabulation provides a clear indication of the overlap between groups for the intermediate rating and the separation of groups at the extremes of the scale. A Chi-Square test (df = 4) demonstrated that the difference between groups for the above distributions of ratings was significant beyond the .01 level.

The estimates of laterality of dysfunction are shown separately for each judge in Table 12. These estimates were made only for the subjects rated by one or both judges as having minimal or definite cerebral dysfunction. Both judges estimated a relatively large proportion of left hemisphere involvement among the Retarded Readers classified as having definite cerebral involvement. Judge A estimated 6 subjects with left hemisphere involvement and only 1 with right hemisphere involvement, with 6 diffuse; and Judge B estimated 12 left and 3 right, with 5 diffuse. This high proportion of estimated left hemisphere involvement did not occur for the Normal Readers classified as definite cerebral dysfunction. Among the Normal Readers, there was 1 rating of left hemisphere and 2 of diffuse involvement by Judge A, with 3 subjects each rated as left, diffuse, and right hemisphere involvement by Judge B. A statistical test of the trend towards ratings of left

TABLE 12

Estimates of degree of lateralization of cerebral dysfunction in subjects rated as having minimal or definite cerebral dysfunction.

	Judge A		Judge B	
Rating	Retarded Readers	Normal Readers	Retarded Readers	Normal Readers
1. Definite Cerebral Dysfunction				
Left hemisphere	0	0	3	1
Left hem. diffuse	6	1	9	2
Diffuse	6	2	5	3
Right hem. diffuse	1	0	1	2
Right hemisphere	0	0	2	1
2. Minimal Cerebral Dysfunction				
Left hemisphere	1	0	4	4
Left hem. diffuse	8	6	3	2
Diffuse	9	13	6	8
Right hem. diffuse	5	3	0	1
Right hemisphere	0	0	1	3

hemisphere involvement in Retarded Readers was precluded by the small number of Normal Readers classified as having definite cerebral dysfunction.

The indication of left hemisphere involvement was not as clear among Retarded Readers classified as minimal cerebral dysfunction, a category for which the judges would not necessarily expect neurological confirmation of test results. Judge A estimated 9 left, 5 right, and 9 diffuse among Retarded Readers, but his ratings of Normal Readers were somewhat comparable: 6 left, 3 right, and 13 diffuse. Judge B estimated 7 left to only 1 right, with 9 diffuse among Retarded Readers, and his ratings of Normal Readers showed a more equal proportion of left and right hemisphere involvement: 6 left, 4 right, and 8 diffuse. If the ratings of the 2 judges for both definite and minimal cerebral dysfunction are taken together, a tendency toward left hemisphere involvement among Retarded Readers is strongly suggested, along with a somewhat lesser incidence of diffuse involvement.

In the course of making the ratings of cerebral dysfunction, Judge A also wrote down his guess as to whether each child had reading disability. These incidental results are worthy of mention because of the remarkable accuracy of prediction:

	Rating by Judge A			
	Reading Disability	*Possible Reading Disability*	*Normal*	*Total*
Retarded Readers	29	4	6	39
Normal Readers	4	3	32	39

A Chi-Square test (df = 2) showed that this difference between groups was significant well beyond the .01 level. It should be noted that even though the nature of the underlying deficit was not described by this procedure, the judgments were based entirely upon test scores from which all direct indications of reading ability had been deleted, and thus represent some uniformity in the test configurations of Retarded Readers.

DISCUSSION

The interpretations were based on incomplete test results (incomplete because of the elimination of all data directly indicative of reading ability), and there were other departures from usual interpretive procedure. Notwithstanding these restrictions, the judges rated a significantly larger proportion of Retarded Readers as exhibiting definite evidence of deviation from normal brain functioning. Thus, if a comparable group of retarded readers was referred for neuropsychological evaluation, it is very likely that a higher-than-normal incidence of probable cerebral dysfunction would be found. Individual differences among retarded readers are suggested by the distribution of pooled ratings, which showed that about one third of the Retarded Readers were placed in the low and intermediate categories of probable cerebral dysfunction to which three fourths of the Normal Readers had been assigned.

The removal of reading-related data from the test results made it especially difficult for the judges to estimate probable lateralization of cerebral dysfunction, since these data may contribute importantly to inferences regarding verbal deficit associated with left hemisphere dysfunction. Even with this restriction, the number of ratings of left hemisphere involvement in Retarded Readers equalled or exceeded the ratings of diffuse involvement by the two judges, and there were relatively few ratings of right hemisphere involvement in Retarded Readers. From these results it can be concluded that test data indicative of cerebral dysfunction in Retarded Readers may further suggest lateralized involvement of the left cerebral hemisphere even when the verbal deficit directly associated with reading disability is disregarded.

The accurate guesses of Judge A regarding the reading status of the subjects suggest that certain distinctive features of the test scores of the Retarded Readers can be recognized by the skilled interpreter. Thus, the retarded reader may be differentiated from the normal reader by the configuration of abilities manifested on a restricted battery of neuropsychological tests.

The test-by-test statistical comparisons described in Chapter 5 did not reveal a configuration of impairment strongly suggestive of lateralized cerebral dysfunction. However, these statistical procedures did not involve a formal analysis of the patterning of test results. Where the patterning of individual test data was taken into consideration by the interpretive method described in the present chapter, a definite implication of left hemisphere involvement did emerge. While the present study did not make full use of the possibilities for differential diagnosis afforded by the interpretive method, a continued use of this method for individual evaluation of patterns of neuropsychological test results in retarded readers should provide a further indication of the incidence of probable cerebral dysfunction and of the extent of apparent left hemisphere involvement. A comparison of the test configurations of retarded readers with those of children having neurologically confirmed cerebral dysfunction would be especially valuable.

CHAPTER EIGHT

Interrelations Among Reading and Non-reading Abilities Compared by Factor Analysis

(IN COLLABORATION WITH JAMES NORTON)

To clarify further the results of test-by-test comparisons of groups, as presented in Chapter 5, factor analyses of a selected set of 79 measures were carried out separately for each group. Factor analysis should reveal the manner in which reading and nonreading skills were interrelated within each group, and a comparison of the factor analyses of the 2 groups should provide additional perspective regarding the pattern of disability of the Retarded Readers. Such a procedure has proven profitable in at least one other study in which the structure of abilities of normal children was compared with the structure of abilities of children with specific disabilities (Farrant, 1964).

The main purposes of the factor analyses in this study were to determine (1) whether a definite reading factor would emerge for each group, (2) whether the groups would differ as to the composition of tests in such a factor, and (3) whether there would be any other gross differences in the organization or the integration of abilities of Retarded Readers and Normal Readers.

The factor analyses were carried out by means of a computer program (BIMD 17, option 1) which could accommodate no more than 79 variables. To meet this requirement, 78 of the most appropriate measures from this study plus age were used for the factor analyses. Measures which were not used included all composite scores, a number of measures with very restricted distributions of scores, and several measures which seemed of especially doubtful relevance to reading disability.

The method of factor analysis used the Principal Components solution for the extraction of factors, a "stopping rule" which retains for rotation all factors whose associated characteristic roots are greater than one, and the "Varimax" solution for rotating the retained factors to an interpretable simple structure. A detailed explanation of the rationale for this procedure is not possible here, and can be obtained from standard texts (cf. Cattell, 1952).

The results of the factor analyses are presented in detailed form in Appendix E (p.176), where the factor loadings of the 79 measures on each of the retained factors are given separately for each group. The first question to be asked of factor analysis pertains to the number of different things that have been measured. Although this question can never be answered with certainty, the number of factors derived should provide a relative indication. The 2 groups were quite comparable in this respect, with 21 factors extracted for Retarded Readers and 23 for Normal Readers. This suggests a similarity in the relative degree of integration of the abilities of the 2 groups.

FACTOR IDENTIFICATION

The Varimax solution gives completely objective orthogonal rotations, which yield uncorrelated factors. This procedure involves rotation of the factors in such a way that each component measure has either a large or a near-zero loading on each factor. Inspection of Appendix E shows that the majority of loadings for each factor tended to be near zero (below .15). The relatively few measures having substantial loadings for a given factor can be easily seen, since factor loadings above .40 and below -.40 have been underlined in Appendix E. The majority of tests with high negative loadings are those in which a high score indicated poor performance.

For both groups a strong factor emerged which could be identified, for present purposes, as reading-spelling ability (Factor 1 in both groups). There was a marked difference between groups in the type of nonreading measures which had high loadings on this factor. This difference was probably the most important finding of the factor analysis and will be discussed in further detail below. The second strongest factor for each group could be identified as visual perceptual speed (Factor 17r in Retarded Readers and Factor 2n in Normal Readers).

Several of the remaining factors for each group could be tentatively named. For the Retarded Readers Factor 4r could be termed a physical maturity factor and Factor 21r might be called constructional or drawing ability. For the Normal Readers both Factor 5n and Factor 12n seemed to relate to somesthetic form perception. The remaining factors for each group were not particularly informative, and there appeared to be no notable differences between groups in the number or the composition of these factors.

Reading-Spelling Factor

The measures most highly correlated with the Reading-Spelling Factor in each group are listed in Table 13. For Retarded Readers there were 27 measures plus Age with loadings beyond .40. All but one of the 7 measures with loadings beyond .80 required reading or spelling. Among the remaining measures, 2 required reading, 13 required visual perceptual speed, 3 required sequential oral responses (Serial Responses, Rhyming Words, and Wechsler-Bellevue Digit Span), and one (Rhythm Test) required sequential auditory perception. These findings provide a very strong suggestion that the reading-spelling ability of Retarded Readers was limited by their deficiency in visual perceptual speed, and that the visual perceptual deficiency might be one aspect of a larger deficiency in the sensory and motor processing of verbal and

TABLE 13

Measures most highly correlated with the reading-spelling factor for each group

Factor lr, Retarded Readers		Factor ln, Normal Readers	
Measure	*Loading*	*Measure*	*Loading*
*88 Sent. Dictation	-93	*2 Spell. Achieve.	87
*2 Spell. Achieve.	91	33 Peabody Pic. Vocab.,	
*87 Oral Spelling	90	oral	86
*1 Read. Achieve.	89	*1 Read. Achieve.	84
*86 Words, Vis. Stim.	-88	*35 Peabody Pic. Vocab.,	
*67 Oral Reading,		written	83
sentences	-87	13 W-B Vocabulary	82
70 Serial Responses	-85	*87 Oral Spelling	78
*35 Peabody Pic. Vocab.,		8 W-B Information	73
written	78	Age	71
**100 Perceptual Speed,		30 Tapping, nonpreferred	59
nonsense syllable	67	60 Sentence Repet.	-58
**99 Perceptual Speed,		54 Grip, preferred	57
nonsense syllable	65	11 W-B Arithmetic	52
**93 Perceptual Speed,		55 Grip, nonpreferred	52
nonsense letter	64	*88 Sent. Dictation	-49
**101 Perceptual Speed,		26 Tact. Performance,	
word	63	location	45
**102 Perceptual Speed, word	58	29 Tapping, preferred	45
**20 Trail Making B	-57	10 W-B Digit Span	44
**96 Perceptual Speed,		*28 Speech Perception	-44
letter in syllable	56		
**18 W-B Digit Symbol	55		
11 W-B Arithmetic	55		
**95 Perceptual Speed,			
letter	54		
*28 Speech Perception	-52		
73 Word Rhyming	51		
**97 Perceptual Speed, two			
letters	50		
10 W-B Digit Span	48		
81 Draw Wheel	48		
**98 Perceptual Speed, form			
sequence	44		
27 Rhythm	44		
Age	43		
**103 Perceptual Speed,			
number	43		
**92 Perceptual Speed, form	41		

*Measures which required reading or spelling
**Measures which required visual perceptual speed
Note: Factor loadings reported to two decimal places, with decimal points omitted.

nonverbal sequences. The clustering of these relatively fundamental skills with reading and spelling seems to demonstrate that the Retarded Readers had not yet mastered some of the basic mechanics of reading. The abilities of Retarded Readers were organized in such a way, then, that reading and spelling skills were associated with certain abilities involving the processing of sequences. These skills of sequential processing were among the nonreading skills in which Retarded Readers were shown to be most severely deficient in the test-by-test analysis reported in Chapter 5.

The interpretation of the Reading-Spelling Factor in Retarded Readers can be further elucidated by a consideration of the Reading-Spelling Factor in Normal Readers. This factor included 17 measures plus Age with loadings beyond .40, as shown in Table 13. Of these, 6 required reading or spelling, 2 were oral vocabulary measures, 3 were Wechsler-Bellevue Verbal subtests, and 4 were measures of gross motor skills (tapping and strength of grip). In definite contrast to the composition of the Reading-Spelling Factor in Retarded Readers, the measures with loadings beyond .80 in Normal Readers included 2 oral vocabulary tests in addition to 3 reading-spelling tasks. Reading and spelling achievement were as closely associated with spoken vocabulary on the Peabody and Wechsler-Bellevue tests as they were with written vocabulary on the Peabody Test. This strongly suggests that reading and spelling skills had evolved in Normal Readers to the point where they were limited only by the child's speaking vocabulary, or perhaps to the point where reading vocabulary became essentially interchangeable with speaking vocabulary. Spoken vocabulary skills, in turn, were associated with certain other verbal skills sampled by the Wechsler-Bellevue Test, and increases of these various aspects of verbal proficiency were associated with physical maturation, as indicated by increases of tapping speed, strength of grip, and age. In the Normal Readers, therefore, reading and spelling skills appeared to be organized in an orderly manner, developing systematically with age and physical maturation and in relation to such relatively abstract skills as speaking vocabulary.

A comparison of the composition of the Reading-Spelling Factor in Retarded Readers and Normal Readers suggests that the Retarded Readers were not hampered in their acquisition of reading and spelling skills by a deficiency of language development, but rather by a deficiency in the rapid processing of visual sequences. The Normal Readers had apparently passed beyond this early stage of reading acquisition, and their skills in reading and spelling had evolved to the level where they were limited only by their present stage of language development.

Visual Perceptual Speed Factor

Table 14 lists for each group the measures with loadings beyond .40 on the factor designated as Visual Perceptual Speed. Of the 11 measures listed for Retarded Readers, 10 were clearly classifiable as

TABLE 14

Measures most highly correlated with the factors designated as visual perceptual speed

Factor 17r, Retarded Readers		Factor 2n, Normal Readers	
Measure	*Loading*	*Measure*	*Loading*
91 Perceptual Speed, number	88	91 Perceptual Speed, number	91
92 Perceptual Speed, form	82	95 Perceptual Speed, letter	85
103 Perceptual Speed, number	80	103 Perceptual Speed, number	83
95 Perceptual Speed, letter	73	92 Perceptual Speed, form	80
97 Perceptual Speed, two letters	60	97 Perceptual Speed, two letters	79
96 Perceptual Speed, letter in syllable	58	96 Perceptual Speed, letter in syllable	70
30 Tapping, nonpreferred	51	100 Perceptual Speed, nonsense syllable	67
18 W-B Digit Symbol	49	18 W-B Digit Symbol	65
93 Perceptual Speed, nonsense letter	48	101 Perceptual Speed, word	63
100 Perceptual Speed, nonsense syllable	42	99 Perceptual Speed, nonsense syllable	62
99 Perceptual Speed, nonsense syllable	41	56 Writing Speed, preferred	-58
		93 Perceptual Speed, nonsense letter	52
		94 Perceptual Speed, gestalt	44

Note: Factor loadings reported to two places, with decimal points omitted.

tasks requiring speed of response to sequences of complex visual stimuli, and the eleventh (tapping speed with nonpreferred hand) was a task requiring a rapid sequence of hand movements. Likewise, 12 of the 13 measures listed for Normal Readers were clearly tasks requiring visual perceptual speed and the thirteenth (writing speed with preferred hand) was a task requiring a rapid sequence of hand movements.

The 2 groups were remarkably similar in the composition of this factor. The somewhat greater strength of the factor in Normal Readers may be related to the absence of a visual perceptual speed component in their Reading-Spelling Factor.

It is quite interesting that a definite visual perceptual speed factor should emerge for both groups in conjunction with the high loadings of visual perceptual speed tasks for the Reading-Spelling Factor in Retarded Readers. Some explanation for this apparently dual role of visual perceptual speed tasks may derive from the coupling of these with tasks requiring rapid hand movements, especially when it is recalled that there was no significant difference between groups for tapping speed and writing speed. There is, of course, no obvious reason why the perceptual speed tasks should be coupled with one type of motor speed task with the preferred hand in one group and another kind of motor speed task with the nonpreferred hand in the other group.

This factor may be interpreted as representing some particular aspect of motor speed, and as such it could be a component of visual perceptual speed on which Retarded Readers were not deficient. Some support for this hypothesis is provided by a more detailed examination of the visual perceptual speed tasks. Those with the highest loadings for both groups for the factor shown in Table 14 involved the relatively simple perceptual tasks of discriminating a single number, letter, or form; while those with highest loadings for the Reading–Spelling Factor of Retarded Readers required the more complex perceptual tasks of discriminating nonsense syllables, nonsense letters, and words.

Other Factors

All the factors derived for each group are listed in Table 15. The

TABLE 15

Gross comparison of factor structure in each group. Factors are listed for each group in the order of their appearance from rotation. The number of measures having loadings beyond .40 are indicated, with a tentative name given for each factor wherever possible.

	Factors for Retarded Readers			Factors for Normal Readers	
No.	No. of Measures beyond .40	Tentative Name	No.	No. of Measures beyond .40	Tentative Name
1	28	READING-SPELLING	1	18	READING-SPELLING
2	4	Wechsler Bellevue Subtests	2	13	VISUAL PERCEPTUAL SPEED
3	2	Tactual Perf. Test			
4	7	Physical Maturity	3	2	Spatial Abilities
5	3	Form Perception	4	3	?
6	3	Form Perception	5	4	Tactual Performance Test
7	3	?	6	6	?
8	3	Memory	7	3	?
9	1	Auditory Rhythm	8	3	Hand ?
10	3	Verbal Skills	9	5	? •
11	2	Writing Speed	10	1	Sentence Formulation
12	1	Perceptual Speed, Form Sequences	11	2	Abstraction
			12	3	Somesthetic Perception
13	2	Hand ?	13	2	Writing
14	2	Somesthetic Perception	14	1	Draw Wheel
15	2	?	15	3	?
16	5	Cognitive ?	16	4	?
17	11	VISUAL PERCEPTUAL SPEED	17	1	Perceptual Speed, Form Sequences
18	2	Verbal	18	3	Wechsler Bellevue Subtests
19	4	?	19	1	Draw House
20	1	Category Test	20	2	Visual
21	5	Constructional Skills	21	4	?
			22	1	Paragraph Comprehension
			23	2	Form Perception

number of measures with loadings above .40 or below -.40 are indicated for each factor. Wherever these measures could reasonably be
subsumed under a common classification, a tentative name was assigned. The 2 groups were quite similar with regard to the number of
measures with high (beyond .40) loadings for each factor, as shown by
the following distributions:

Retarded Readers		Normal Readers	
No. of Measures with High Loadings	Number of Factors	No. of Measures with High Loadings	Number of Factors
28	1	18	1
11	1	13	1
7	1	6	1
5	2	5	1
4	2	4	3
3	5	3	6
2	6	2	5
1	3	1	5
	21		23

The only factors for which there were more than 10 measures with high
loadings were the Reading-Spelling and Visual Perceptual Speed factors
discussed in the previous sections. Otherwise, the majority of factors
in each group had 5 or fewer measures with high loadings.

The names given to factors were arbitrary. The measures entering into these designations can be determined by reference to Appendix
E. In some cases no common feature could be found for naming a factor. There were a number of factors besides Reading-Spelling and Visual Perceptual Speed which seemed very similar in composition for
the 2 groups. Factor 18n (Wechsler-Bellevue subtests) for Normal
Readers was similar in composition to Factor 2r (Wechsler-Bellevue
subtests) and also to Factor 18r (Verbal) for Retarded Readers. Factor 3r and Factor 5n both had high loadings on subtests of the Tactual
Performance Test. Factors 5r and 23n had high loadings on tests which
required memory for forms. Factors 12r and 17n both had a high loading on only one test, Measure 98 (visual perceptual speed, sequence of
geometric forms). Factors 14r and 12n had high loadings on several
tests requiring somesthetic perception. Finally, Factor 9r had a high
loading on only the Rhythm Test and Factor 20r had a high loading only
on the Category Test, whereas Factor 11n had high loadings only on the
2 tests together.

While the factorial structures obtained for the 2 groups were far
from identical, there was enough similarity in certain gross aspects of
the analyses to suggest that there were no marked differences in the
overall organization or in the integration of the abilities of the two
groups.

CONCLUSIONS

The results of factor analysis must be interpreted with caution, as several writers (Coan, 1964; Overall, 1964) have recently pointed out. Factor analysis provides a means of reducing a large number of correlated measures to a smaller and more comprehensible set of uncorrelated factors, but such factors do not necessarily represent primary abilities, concrete causes, faculties, traits, or specific mental energies. And the stability of factors is best ascertained by reapplication of the same set of measures to a new sample of subjects.

The results of the factor analyses carried out in this study seem quite clear even when interpreted in the conservative manner recommended by Coan and Overall. With reference to the three main purposes of the analyses, as stated at the beginning of this chapter, the following answers can be given: (1) A definite reading factor did emerge as the strongest factor for each group; (2) there were very pronounced differences between groups in the composition of this factor, with measures of visual perceptual speed and other sequential processing skills associated with reading and spelling ability in Retarded Readers, and measures of oral vocabulary and other verbal skills associated with reading and spelling in Normal Readers; and (3) there were no other gross differences between Retarded Readers and Normal Readers in the organization and integration of abilities, as indicated by the distribution and composition of factors obtained for the 2 groups.

The main reservation in the interpretation of these results relates to replication. There is no guarantee that the most important finding — a difference between groups in the composition of the Reading-Spelling Factor — was not attributable to accidents of sampling in either or both groups. Unfortunately, in this study as in many others there were a number of insurmountable practical problems which prevented any attempt at replication.

Despite the limitations necessarily imposed upon any conclusions drawn from the factor analyses, these results provided a very valuable adjunct to the test-by-test analysis of covariance. The suggestion that deficiencies of reading acquisition in Retarded Readers are associated with deficiencies of visual perceptual speed rather than general language retardation provided, for the first time in this study, some indication of the manner in which reading disability might be considered specific in Retarded Readers. The arrest of Retarded Readers at an early stage of reading acquisition may well be integrally associated with arrest at an early stage of perceptual maturation.

These findings should provide definite suggestions for further investigation of the possible limitations imposed by deficient maturation of sequential processing skills.

Differentiation of Groups on Non-reading Measures by Multiple Stepwise Regression and Discriminant Analysis

(IN COLLABORATION WITH JAMES NORTON)

The difference between groups for individual measures was assessed by analysis of covariance (Chapter 4), and the interrelationships among measures within each group were assessed by factor analysis (Chapter 8). The results of 2 additional statistical procedures, multiple stepwise regression analysis and discriminant analysis, are reported in the present chapter. Both of these methods involve multiple correlation. The purpose of each, as employed here, was to indicate the degree to which Retarded Readers were differentiated from Normal Readers by specific sets of nonreading measures.

In multiple stepwise regression analysis the measure which produces the greatest increase in the differentiation between groups is added at each step of the analysis. For a given set of measures, the single measure which best differentiates 2 groups in terms of the F ratio between groups is selected first. Then at each subsequent step of the analysis the measure which increases the differentiation between groups by the greatest amount is added. After the first step, however, the contribution of a given measure is not determined by its differentiating power as an individual test, since the part of a test's potential discriminating power that is correlated with previously selected measures will add nothing to the total differentiation. Rather, the amount of contribution by a given measure as it is added to previously selected measures is determined by its unique or uncorrelated differentiating power. Thus, if 2 tests were perfectly correlated, only one of them would be selected during multiple stepwise regression analysis, since the other would add nothing unique to the differentiation of groups. This procedure, then, arranges tests according to their relative contribution to the differentiation of groups. Although certain problems arose in the interpretation of results, the stepwise regression analysis provided a somewhat different means of assessing the relative importance of the nonreading deficit associated with reading disability.

Discriminant analysis is used to determine the maximum amount that 2 groups can be separated by fixed sets of tests. For each set of tests the single weighted score is derived which produces a maximum separation of groups. This single weighted score is obtained by summation of the differentially weighted scores of individual tests. Measures which tend to make the greatest unique contribution to the differentiation of groups would receive the highest weights. By this procedure the maximum predictive ability of any set of tests as applied to a particular comparison of groups can be calculated. The main reason for computing discriminant analyses in the present study was to determine the degree of precision with which reading status could be predicted by various sets of nonreading measures. Both multiple stepwise regression analysis and discriminant analysis, then, were used to gain further insight into the nonreading deficiencies of Retarded Readers as a group.

MULTIPLE STEPWISE REGRESSION ANALYSIS

Computations for the multiple stepwise regression analysis were carried out by the BIMD 34 computer program. This program allowed the use of no more than 57 variables. In the selection of these variables all measures that required any form of reading or spelling were excluded, as were the nonverbal IQ measures on which the groups had been equated. The 57 measures selected for this analysis included the Verbal subtests of the Wechsler-Bellevue Scale (Measures 8-13); several tests of lateral dominance (Measures 51-55); all measures from Halstead's Category, Tactual Performance, Rhythm, and Tapping Tests (Measures 21-27, 29, and 30); 15 measures from the Minnesota Aphasia Test (Measures 60, 62, 63, 68-70, and 73-81); 8 measures of sensory and perceptual disturbances (Measures 41-46, 49, and 50); 4 drawing tasks from the Halstead-Wepman Aphasia Screening Test (Measures 36-39); 3 tests of visual perceptual speed (Measures 92, 94, 98); and Oral Picture Vocabulary (33), Reversals (105), Visual Spatial and Temporal Memory (108, 109), Color Form (107), Word Association (106), and Spatial Orientation (104). In addition, the variable of Age was forced into the analysis as a control variable at the first step to increase the sensitivity of the analysis by reducing the influence of age variation within groups.

As described above, the stepwise regression procedure selected the measure which best discriminated the 2 groups, and then selected the measure which provided the greatest increase of discrimination on subsequent steps. The computer program was automatically terminated at a step where the amount of increase in discrimination fell below a certain predetermined value. The degree of differentiation between groups was indicated by the magnitude of a multiple correlation coefficient, since the regression analysis actually involved calculation of the correlation between the selected variables and reading status at each step. Reading status, for this purpose, was considered to have only 2 values, with each Retarded Reader assigned a value of 0 and each Normal Reader assigned a value of 1. The greater the difference between groups for a given combination of measures, then, the higher would be the multiple correlation coefficient at that step.

Table 16 shows the 29 measures selected by the multiple stepwise regression analysis, arranged according to their order of selection,

TABLE 16

Measures added at each step of the multiple stepwise regression analysis to maximize the multiple correlation with reading status. The higher the multiple correlation, the greater the difference between Retarded Readers (Reading Status = 0) and Normal Readers (Reading Status = 1). Age was forced in as a control variable at the first step.

Step No.	Measure Added	Multiple Correlation Coefficient
1	Age	.021
2	73. Minnesota Aphasia: Rhyming	.767
3	13. Wechsler-Bellevue: Vocabulary	.862
4	105. Thurstone Reversals	.882
5	92. Visual Perceptual Speed: Single Form	.892
6	22. Tactual Performance Test: Preferred Hand	.901
7	50. Astereognosis: Left Hand	.909
8	68. Minnesota Aphasia: Articulation	.914
9	81. Minnesota Aphasia: Reproduce Wheel	.920
10	80. Minnesota Aphasia: Draw Man	.925
11	37. Halstead-Wepman Aphasia: Draw Cross	.930
12	8. Wechsler-Bellevue: Information	.933
13	39. Halstead-Wepman Aphasia: Copy Key	.936
14	36. Halstead-Wepman Aphasia: Copy Square	.940
15	23. Tactual Performance Test, Nonpreferred Hand	.943
16	46. Finger Agnosia: Left Hand	.945
17	63. Minnesota Aphasia: Matching Forms	.946
18	49. Astereognosis: Right Hand	.948
19	44. Visual Suppression: Left Hand	.949
20	42. Tactile Suppression: Left Hand	.950
21	75. Minnesota Aphasia: Picture Description	.951
22	104. Spatial Orientation	.952
23	69. Minnesota Aphasia: Sentence Completion	.953
24	77. Minnesota Aphasia: Retell Paragraph	.954
25	33. Peabody Oral Picture Vocabulary	.954
26	38. Halstead-Wepman Aphasia: Copy Triangle	.955
27	54. Grip Strength: Preferred Hand	.955
28	53. Foot Preference	.956
29	107. Color Form	.956

along with the multiple correlation between reading status and the measures included at each step. It will be noted that a multiple correlation of .90, which would account for over 80 percent of the difference between groups in reading status, was achieved after the first 5 tests (excluding age) had been added. The remaining 23 steps increased the multiple correlation to .96, accounting for a total of 92 percent of the difference between groups in reading status. Thus, the reading status of Normal Readers and Retarded Readers was very highly correlated with a set of 28 nonreading measures, with the largest contribution to the differentiation of groups made by the first measures that were added.

The results presented in Table 16 must be interpreted with some caution. After age had been forced in, the first measure added to the multiple regression equation was the measure which *by itself* best differentiated the 2 groups. This step could have been predicted by reference to Appendix C (p. 169) to determine which of the 57 nonreading measures used for Multiple Stepwise Regression Analysis had received the highest F' ratio in the analysis of individual test results. This was the Rhyming Test (F = 107). Thus, the nonreading skill which by itself provided the best prediction of reading status was the ability to rhyme single words. Appendix C shows that the nonreading test with the next highest F' ratio was the Wechsler-Bellevue Information Subtest (F = 99). However, this test was not added at the next step of multiple regression. After the Rhyming Test, all subsequent steps were those which added the most to the prediction provided by the tests selected up to that step. As stated above, the higher the correlation between a given test and previously selected measures the less it would add to the multiple correlation, even though it might discriminate the groups very well as an individual test. Thus, a number of nonreading tests which were highly discriminative as individual measures were not selected at all because of the high correlation of their power to discriminate reading status with that of previously selected measures. Such tests included Wechsler-Bellevue Similarities, Serial Responses (Naming of Months), the Seashore Rhythm Test, the 2 visual memory tests, and the oral form of the Peabody Picture Vocabulary Test.

The manner in which the relative contributions of not-yet-included measures changed as a function of the measures added at each step of multiple stepwise regression is shown in Table 17. The measures added at the first 12 steps of analysis are listed, plus 5 non-selected measures which were highly discriminating as individual tests. In the body of the table a measure designated as the F ratio for selection is given for each non-selected measure at each of the first 12 steps. The F ratios for selection at any given step provide a relative indication of the unique differentiating power that each non-selected measure could contribute at that stage of the analysis.

At Step 1, after Age had been forced in, all F ratios had the identical values obtained by the analysis of covariance for individual measures (Appendix C). Since the Rhyming Test had the highest F ratio for selection, it was selected at Step 2. With the addition of the Rhyming Test, all of the discriminating power that the non-selected tests shared with the Rhyming Test was, in effect, subtracted from their respective F ratios for selection on Step 2. The Information subtest, which had had the next highest F ratio at Step 1, must have shared considerable discriminating power with the Rhythm Test, since its F ratio was reduced by two thirds on Step 2. Likewise, large reductions of F ratio occurred for the majority of the other measures which had had large F ratios on Step 1. Whatever basic impairment of ability had led to the poor performance of Retarded Readers on the Rhyming Test must have also contributed heavily to their deficiency on a variety of other nonreading skills, including the discrimination of reversed figures, visual perceptual speed, drawing a man, verbalizing similarities, naming months, perception of auditory rhythm, and visual memory.

The only measure which had an initially high F ratio on Step 1 and did not decrease sharply on Step 2 was the Wechsler-Bellevue Vocabulary Test. This measure was added to Rhythm and Age at Step 3,

TABLE 17

Changes in the F ratio for selection over the first 12 steps of multiple stepwise regression, with F ratios shown at each step for the first 12 measures selected, plus five additional measures which were highly discriminating in test-by-test statistical analyses.

Measure	F'* Rank	Mult. Corr.	Step 1	2	3	4	5	6	7	8	9	10	11	12
							F for Selection							
Age (forced in)		.021	ADD											
73. Word Rhyming	6	.767	107.3	ADD										
13. W-B Vocabulary	13	.862	45.8	44.1	ADD									
105. Reversals	20	.882	25.9	4.2	11.6	ADD								
92. Perceptual Speed, form	27	.892	19.4	4.4	5.2	6.4	ADD							
22. Tact. Performance, preferred	R	.901	15.9	8.6	5.0	6.2	5.8	ADD						
50. Astereog., left	R	.909	4.4	7.8	7.3	5.7	5.6	5.8	ADD					
68. Articulation	28	.914	18.0	8.0	2.7	3.5	3.3	4.2	4.4	ADD				
81. Draw Wheel	n.s.	.920	3.6	0.4	1.1	3.3	3.2	3.9	3.3	4.9	ADD			
80. Draw Man	25	.925	20.6	1.8	8.2	4.2	4.9	5.3	3.3	3.2	4.0	ADD		
37. Copy Cross	57	.930	4.2	0.2	0.1	0.6	0.2	0.1	0.6	1.6	0.9	4.5	ADD	
8. W-B Information	7	.933	99.0	31.0	6.6	4.6	3.6	2.1	2.1	1.4	1.8	2.3	3.0	ADD
12. W-B Similarities	12		51.8	15.8	4.7	4.2	3.6	1.5	2.5	1.9	1.4	0.9	0.7	0.1
70. Serial Responses	16		46.2	2.7	2.9	3.3	2.0	1.6	1.0	0.3	0.7	1.5	0.7	0.6
27. Rhythm	21		25.2	4.5	1.9	0.6	0.8	0.4	0.2	0.3	0.0	0.0	0.0	0.0
109. Visual Temporal Memory	24		20.9	4.7	3.1	0.2	0.4	0.4	0.7	0.2	0.1	0.3	0.5	0.0
33. Peabody Pic. Vocab., oral	33		17.9	9.2	0.0	0.2	0.1	0.0	0.2	0.0	0.0	0.1	0.0	0.3

*Numerical Rank assigned according to size of F' ratio obtained by analysis of covariance (see Table 5) for measures on which Normal Readers were superior. "n.s." designates measures on which groups did not differ significantly, and "R" designates measures on which Retarded Readers were significantly superior.

increasing the multiple correlation from .767 to .862. The relatively large increase in differentiating power suggested that a deficiency of some more general language ability existed separately from the deficiency of rhyming ability in Retarded Readers. At the same time, the addition of Wechsler-Bellevue Vocabulary at Step 3 served to decrease the potential contribution of several of the remaining variables, as shown by comparison of F ratios for selection for Steps 2 and 3. The 3 measures which had had the next highest F ratios on Step 2 were all sharply reduced, with Information decreasing from 31.0 to 6.6, Similarities from 15.8 to 4.7, and Peabody Oral Vocabulary from 9.2 to 0. The potential contribution of all 3 measures was closely associated with that of Wechsler-Bellevue Vocabulary as especially indicated by the elimination of the differentiating power of the other vocabulary measure.

The addition of Vocabulary at Step 3 actually "released" additional differentiating power in the Reversals Test, which was then selected at Step 4. From this point on the successive changes of the F ratios of non-selected measures at each step were less dramatic. The rather unexpected increases in some cases occurred for relatively complicated reasons that are irrelevant to the main issues here. It suffices to say that a more careful preselection of measures would have simplified the interpretation of the results of stepwise multiple regression analysis.

The major classes of nonreading skill that were related to reading status by multiple stepwise regression are perhaps best indicated by examination of the first 5 tests selected, which were highly predictive of reading status. As discussed above, the ability to rhyme words was selected as the most discriminative measure, and this ability was highly correlated in differentiating power with several non-selected measures. The skills which added most to rhyming in predicting reading status were spoken vocabulary, the visual discrimination of reversed figures, speed of visual perception of a single form, and speed of somesthetic form discrimination. Both rhyming and spoken vocabulary exemplify the verbal input tasks on which Retarded Readers were particularly deficient; and the visual perceptual speed and reversals tasks exemplify the visual input tasks on which Retarded Readers were equally deficient. It should also be noted that both rhyming and visual perceptual speed were highly correlated with the Reading-Spelling Factor of Retarded Readers but not of Normal Readers; and that Vocabulary was highly correlated with the Reading-Spelling Factor of Normal Readers but not of Retarded Readers. The Tactual Performance Test, of course, provided the most striking suggestion of a relative predominance of somesthetic skills in Retarded Readers.

The results of stepwise multiple regression analysis, like the results of factor analysis, would best be verified by a replication study. If we could accept the present groups as truly representative of the underlying populations of Retarded Readers and Normal Readers, these results would provide a further suggestion that reading retardation is associated with nonreading deficiencies in the processing of temporal sequences, in the emission of language behavior, in certain visual pattern discriminations, and in rapid sequential visual discriminations, along with superiority in processes which require somesthetic discrimination. This set of nonreading deficiencies would be inferred for Retarded Readers as a group. The discriminant analyses reported below give a clearer indication of the predictive power of various sets of measures for separating the group distributions.

DISCRIMINANT ANALYSIS

Discriminant analyses were performed for 2 different sets of measures. The first set comprised the nonreading measures selected by multiple stepwise regression analysis, and the second set was arbitrarily selected to answer specific questions regarding the nonreading characteristics of Retarded Readers. The discriminant analyses were executed by use of the BIMD 05 computer program.

In contrast to multiple stepwise regression analysis, which increases the differentiation between groups as each new measure is added to a set of tests, discriminant analysis selects a configuration of weighted scores which produces a maximum separation of 2 groups for a fixed set of tests.

The following steps are involved in discriminant analysis:

1. A fixed set of tests is selected for analysis.

2. The 2 groups to be differentiated are treated as a two-valued variable (e.g., reading retardation = 0, normal reading = 1). A multiple correlation is computed between the set of tests and this two-valued variable. The size of the squared multiple correlation coefficient, R^2, indicates the strength of the discrimination between the two values of the variable.

3. The multiple correlation procedure also results in the assignment of differential weights to the tests which comprise the set.

4. A single score is calculated for each subject in each group by summation of the differentially weighted scores of individual tests.

5. All subjects are ranked according to this single weighted score, and the discriminating power of the differentially weighted tests can be demonstrated in terms of the amount of overlap in the rankings of the 2 groups.

Discriminant Analysis with Nonreading Measure
Selected by Multiple Stepwise Regression

This series of discriminant analyses was performed with the 25 measures selected in the first 25 steps of the multiple stepwise regression, since this was the maximum number of measures for which the computer program could perform discriminant analysis. Discriminant analysis was performed for the total set of 25 measures, and also

TABLE 18

Summary of the results of discriminant analyses of the sets of measures selected by multiple stepwise regression analysis

Sets of Measures Selected by step-wise Regression (see Table 16)	R^2	Estimated Proportion of Overlap in Populations	Actual Overlap in Present Samples	
			Retarded Readers Misclas-sified	Normal Readers Misclas-sified
First 2	.588	.119	9	10
3	.743	.047	3	1
4	.778	.032	1	1
5	.796	.026	0	0
6	.812	.020	0	0
7	.826	.016	0	0
8	.835	.013	0	0
9	.846	.010	0	0
10	.856	.008	0	0
11	.865	.006	0	0
14	.884	.003	0	0
18	.899	.002	0	0
21	.904	.001	0	0
23	.908	.001	0	0
25 steps	.911	.001	0	0

for 14 subsets drawn from the first 2, 3, 4, 5, 6, 7, 8, 9, 10, 11, 14, 18, 21, and 23 steps of the multiple stepwise regression analysis (the measures selected at each of these steps are listed in Table 16, p. 102).

The results of these discriminant analyses are summarized in Table 18. Shown for each subset are the squared multiple correlation coefficient (R^2), the estimated proportion of overlap in the populations from which the samples of Retarded Readers and Normal Readers were drawn, and the actual overlap between groups. As stated previously, R^2 indicates the strength of the discrimination between groups. It should also be noted that the R^2 for each step listed in Table 18 is simply the squared value of the multiple correlation coefficient for that step in the multiple stepwise regression analysis, as shown in Table 16. Thus, the strength of discrimination as computed by discriminant analysis is exactly the same as that computed by multiple stepwise regression analysis. Whereas the multiple stepwise regression analysis sorted tests according to their unique discriminating power, the discriminant analysis provided additional details regarding the degree of separation between groups for fixed sets of tests.

The additional details of greatest interest were the estimated proportion of overlap of populations and the actual overlap of weighted scores between the present groups. If it is assumed that the underlying populations from which the present samples of Retarded Readers and Normal Readers were drawn were normally distributed with respect to a given set of weighted scores, the "estimated proportion of overlap" refers to the proportion of individuals in each population who would fall within the other population when all members of both populations were ranked according to the weighted score determined by discriminant analysis. It can be seen from Table 18 that a proportion of only .001, or one in 1,000 members, of the hypothetical underlying populations of Retarded Readers and Normal Readers would be misclassified (fall within the other population) by the weighted scores computed for the sets of measures included at Steps 25, 23, and 21 of the multiple stepwise regression. Only one in 100 misclassifications would occur with the weighted scores based on the 9 measures included at Step 9, only 2 in 100 with the 6 measures included at Step 6, and fewer than 5 misclassifications in 100 with the 3 measures included at Step 3. Thus, the hypothetical underlying populations of Retarded and Normal Readers would be well separated even when the discriminant analysis included only age plus the first 2 measures (Rhyming and Wechsler-Bellevue Vocabulary) selected by multiple stepwise regression analysis.

The actual overlap between groups was obtained by ranking subjects according to the weighted scores obtained by discriminant analysis. As Table 18 shows, the groups were completely separated for all except the first 3 subsets. Where as few as four measures (Rhyming, Wechsler-Bellevue Vocabulary, Reversals, and Visual Perceptual Speed for Forms) plus age were included, the lowest scoring Normal Reader ranked higher than the highest scoring Retarded Reader. And even at Step 3 only one Normal Reader fell within the distribution of Retarded Readers and 3 Retarded Readers within the distribution of Normal Readers.

With sets of measures preselected by multiple stepwise regression analysis, the Retarded Readers could be completely differentiated from Normal Readers on the basis of discriminant analysis of nonreading skills alone. This demonstrated the lack of specificity of reading disability in the present sample of Retarded Readers and indicated the direction of nonreading impairment. These results also illustrate the usefulness of multiple regression techniques for predicting reading difficulty on the basis of nonreading skills.

Discriminant Analysis of Arbitrarily Selected Nonreading Measures

A second series of discriminant analyses was carried out with subsets of 18 measures arbitrarily selected to assess their combined differentiating power. These were selected from tests on which Normal Readers were significantly superior to Retarded Readers, excluding tests which required any skill that might be classified as reading or spelling. The 18 nonreading measures selected, arranged according to their discriminating power as individual tests, were as follows:

     73. Minnesota Aphasia: Rhyming
      8. Wechsler-Bellevue: Information
     12. Wechsler-Bellevue: Similarities
     70. Minnesota Aphasia: Serial Responses (Months)
     13. Wechsler-Bellevue: Vocabulary
   105. Thurstone Reversals
     27. Seashore Rhythm
   109. Visual Temporal Memory
     80. Minnesota Aphasia: Draw a Man
   108. Visual Spatial Memory
     92. Visual Perceptual Speed: Single Form
     68. Minnesota Aphasia: Articulation
     33. Peabody Picture Vocabulary, Oral Presentation
     78. Minnesota Aphasia: Copy Complex Figure
     77. Minnesota Aphasia: Retell Paragraph
     60. Minnesota Aphasia: Oral Sentence Repetition
      9. Wechsler-Bellevue: Comprehension
     10. Wechsler-Bellevue: Digit Span

It will be noted that this set of tests, in contrast to the sets selected from the multiple stepwise regression, did not include age as a control variable and did not include any tests on which Retarded Readers were superior to Normal Readers.

Seven subsets of tests were selected for additional discriminant analysis from the 18 tests listed above. These subsets were used to test hypotheses regarding nonreading deficits of Retarded Readers. Thus, this series of discriminant analyses was not intended to derive a maximum discrimination of groups, but rather to assess the discriminating power of small, arbitrarily grouped subsets of nonreading tests. The subsets can be described as follows:

Subset 1 (Verbal Subtests) consisted of 5 verbal subtests from the Wechsler-Bellevue Scale.

Subset 2 (Easily Administered) included 5 oral subtests from the Minnesota Aphasia Test that can be easily administered and scored (Rhyming, Naming Months, Articulation, Sentence Repetition, and Retelling Paragraph).

Subset 3 (Visual) included 4 visual nonverbal tasks (Thurstone Reversals, Visual Perceptual Speed: Single Form, Visual Spatial Memory, and Visual Temporal Memory).

Subset 4 (Visual-Motor) included 3 visual-motor tasks (Copy Complex Figure, Draw Man, and Visual Perceptual Speed: Single Form).

Subset 5 (Complex Discrimination) included one measure each of complex visual and complex auditory discrimination (Seashore Rhythm and Thurstone Reversals).

Subset 6 (Memory) included 2 tests each of visual and auditory memory (Digit Span, Sentence Repetition, Visual Spatial Memory, and Visual Temporal Memory).

TABLE 19

Summary of the results of discriminant analyses of arbitrarily selected sets of nonreading measures

Subsets		Estimated Proportion of Overlap in Populations	Actual Overlap in Present Samples	
			Retarded Readers Misclassified	Normal Readers Misclassified
Designation	No. of Measures			
Full Set	18	.034	2	5
1. Verbal sub.	5	.145	25	19
2. Easily Adm.	5	.101	9	10
3. Visual	4	.215	16	31
4. Visual-Motor	3	.238	28	15
5. Visual & Aud. Discrimination	2	.241	23	33
6. Memory	4	.265	25	38
7. Sequential Stored Inform.	2	.117	17	28

Subset 7 (Sequential Stored Information) included 2 tests of sequential stored information (Rhyming and Serial Responses: Months).

The results of these discriminant analyses are summarized in Table 19. It is immediately apparent that the measures, arbitrarily chosen because of their "face validity," did not approach the precision of discrimination of the measures selected according to the multiple stepwise regression analysis. Only for the entire set of 18 tests was the estimated population overlap below 5 percent, and the estimated overlap was more than 20 percent for 4 of the subsets. This disparity was even more pronounced when expressed in terms of the actual overlap between the weighted scores of Normal and Retarded Readers. The total overlap of 5 subjects for the entire set of 18 measures in Table 19 was greater than the total overlap of 4 subjects for only the first 2 measures plus age (Step 3 in Table 18) selected by stepwise multiple regression analysis.

Therefore, when certain measures were grouped according to arbitrary criteria, the resulting discriminant functions did not separate Retarded Readers from Normal Readers with nearly the precision of the measures derived by the generalized stepwise regression analysis. This suggests that none of the arbitrary groupings represented a cluster of abilities consistently associated with retarded reading. These results also demonstrate that any battery of measures for predicting reading disability should be derived by multivariate correlational analyses rather than the usual arbitrary procedures of selection and weighting.

CONCLUSIONS

Multiple stepwise regression analyses and discriminant analyses provided additional perspectives for evaluating the nonreading impairment of Retarded Readers. The test-by-test analysis of covariance had shown a widespread impairment of nonreading skills with an especially severe deficiency of visual and verbal skills, and the results of factor analysis had further suggested that the reading achievement of Retarded Readers was apparently limited by their deficiency in visual perceptual speed but not by their deficiency in certain spoken language abilities. The multiple stepwise regression analysis revealed that of the nonreading measures, 2 spoken language abilities contributed the greatest amount to the differentiation of Retarded Readers from Normal Readers, with the next greatest amount contributed by 2 visual abilities.

The discriminant analyses further demonstrated that the 2 groups could be almost completely separated by weighted scores derived from the 2 language measures mentioned above plus age, and the separation of groups became complete when the 2 visual nonreading measures were included in discriminant analysis.

Exactly how much of the apparent differentiating power of various nonreading measures was attributable to accidents of sampling could not be established without a repetition of these procedures with new samples of Retarded Readers and Normal Readers. Ideally, the test battery should be modified, readministered, and reanalyzed several times by multivariate analytical procedures until a set of clearly interpretable measures is derived. Such a set of measures should then provide a concise description of the patterns of reading and nonreading skills associated with various forms of reading difficulty, and should permit prediction of reading deficiencies on the basis of relatively small sets of nonreading tests.

For the present, the collective results of the 4 types of statistical analysis suggest the following tentative description of the configuration of reading and nonreading impairment associated with specific reading disability:

1. Reading disability was associated with impairment of a wide variety of nonreading skills.

2. The most consistent nonreading impairment occurred in certain types of visual task and certain types of verbal task, although other visual tasks and verbal tasks were performed at a normal level.

3. The Retarded Readers were shown to be as sharply differentiated from Normal Readers by optimal, weighted scores for a small set of nonreading tasks (oral word rhyming, oral vocabulary, discrimination of reversed figures, and speed of perception of visual forms, plus age) as they were by the original criterion of reading ability (see Table 2, p. 22).

4. However, the reading acquisition of Retarded Readers was not directly affected by all of their nonreading deficiencies. Their reading impairment seemed to be directly associated, and perhaps limited, by deficiencies on tasks which required sequential processing, such as speed of visual perception of sequences of forms and sequential naming of verbal sequences. Reading ability did not seem to be directly limited by the deficiencies of Retarded Readers in spoken verbal skills such as oral vocabulary and general information.

5. It may be suggested at this point that the visual and verbal impairment of Retarded Readers could be attributable to a common abnormality of birth or development, perhaps some form of maturational defect. However, the acquisition of reading was only directly affected by those skills directly required for the first stages of reading. Since beginning reading involves the sequential processing of associated visual and verbal material, the nonreading deficiencies most directly impairing acquisition would be visual and verbal sequential skills. Although the Retarded Readers were almost equally impaired in other visual (e.g., form memory) and verbal (e.g., oral vocabulary) skills, these skills were sufficiently developed so as not to interfere with early reading acquisition. However, it must be assumed that if the sequential processing difficulty were overcome, the reading ability of Retarded Readers would then develop to a point where it was still limited well below the point of normal reading achievement by the deficiency of speaking vocabulary.

The above explanation of the complex manifestations of the pattern of nonreading deficiency in Retarded Readers may bear little resemblance to whatever final explanation is derived for specific reading disability. The desirability of replication has been mentioned several times. The terms "visual" and "verbal," which figure prominently in the explanation, are disturbingly ambiguous. However, the multifaceted statistical analysis appeared to have added greatly to the descriptive power of the explanation of nonreading impairment. The continued application of more advanced multiple statistical techniques should be adopted as one approach to increased understanding of severe reading problems. At the same time, other approaches which involve completely different strategies of analysis should be vigorously pursued. The search for simple, parsimonious explanations of reading disability over several generations appears to have been largely fruitless, and the possibility that this serious disorder is complex and multidimensional must now be assessed by the best tools of experimental analysis that are currently available.

CHAPTER TEN

Individual Differences Among
Retarded Readers

If reading disability were associated with different types of nonreading impairment from one Retarded Reader to another, these individual differences could have become apparent in several ways. To take as examples 2 of the most likely types of selective nonreading impairment, there could have been a "perceptual type," whose reading difficulty was primarily associated with deficiencies of visual perception, and a "language type," with a primary deficiency of language development. If these individual differences had represented truly selective impairment, the perceptual type of Retarded Reader should have been normal or near normal in verbal nonreading abilities, and the language type of Retarded Reader should have been normal or near normal in visual nonreading abilities. Thus, the scores of Retarded Readers would have been much more variable than the scores of Normal Readers for the visual and verbal nonreading measures, resulting in much larger standard deviations for Retarded Readers on visual and verbal nonreading measures. Inspection of the entries in column 4 of Appendix C (p.169) shows that this was not the case. Except for a few cases where the distributions for Normal Readers were restricted by a high proportion of perfect scores, the groups did not differ greatly in standard deviation. This suggests that where impairment of a given nonreading skill occurred, it took the form of a downward shift of the entire distribution of scores for Retarded Readers as compared with Normal Readers. Such uniformity would leave little room for distinct typologies within the group of Retarded Readers.

Likewise, if there had been pronounced individual differences among Retarded Readers, the nonreading tests associated with the various "types" of reading disability should not have received high loadings on the reading-spelling factor which emerged for the Retarded Reader group, since these tests would have been correlated with reading skills only for subsets of children within the group. As it turned out, the loadings of nonreading tests on the reading-spelling factor for Retarded Readers were as high or higher than the nonreading test loadings on the corresponding factor for Normal Readers. This suggests that a uniform pattern of nonreading deficit was correlated with reading ability in Retarded Readers; those subjects who were least impaired in reading skills tended to be least impaired in associated nonreading skills, and subjects with the most severe reading disability tended to have the most severe deficit of associated non-reading skills.

There seemed to be a striking uniformity among Retarded Readers with regard to patterns of associated nonreading deficiencies. In addition to the inferences drawn from standard deviations of individual tests and from factor analysis, the results of the individual analyses of cerebral dysfunction previously reported in Chapter 7 also failed to reveal any pronounced subgroupings of Retarded Readers. In spite of the apparent absence of marked individual differences among Retarded Readers, however, the interpretation of the present study would not be complete without some consideration of the Retarded Readers as individuals. It is often very difficult to relate studies which report only group findings to explanations of reading disability that are based on individual reports of representative cases. Fairly detailed descriptions of test results and case findings for 9 of the Retarded Readers are presented in this chapter in order to provide a context for considering the results of the present study in relation to previous case studies. At the same time, these individual descriptions should afford a broader perspective for evaluation of the group data.

METHOD OF INDIVIDUAL ANALYSIS

A set of 25 reading and nonreading measures was selected to represent the classes of skill that most clearly differentiated Retarded Readers from Normal Readers. The scores obtained by the group of Normal Readers for each of these measures were converted from absolute values to percentiles. Then the scores of each Retarded Reader selected for individual analysis were expressed in terms of these percentiles. For each measure considered, then, the performance of each Retarded Reader could be evaluated in terms of where he would be placed in a group of Normal Readers. However, none of the measures were age-corrected. This means that a normal performance for a younger Normal Reader would tend to fall somewhat below the 50th percentile, which is representative of average performance, and a normal performance for an older Normal Reader would tend to fall somewhat above the 50th percentile. Except for this slight reservation, the expression of scores in terms of percentile of the Normal Readers permitted a very straightforward evaluation of individual profiles.

SELECTION OF RETARDED READERS
FOR INDIVIDUAL ANALYSIS

The 9 Retarded Readers were chosen to represent problems of several different types. Subjects 1 and 2 appeared to exemplify the type of specific disability with which this investigation was primarily concerned: normal nonverbal intelligence with severe, intractable reading retardation. Subjects 3 and 4 were children whose reading problem could have involved genetic transmission, since each had a father with a history of reading disability. Subject 5 represented an individual whose reading difficulty occurred in spite of exceptionally high nonverbal intelligence. Subject 6 provided the best example of a child with reading disability whose verbal intelligence appeared to be at about the same level as his nonverbal intelligence. Subjects 7 and 8 were fraternal twins who both met the criteria of specific reading disability. And Subject 9 provided an example of a child whose reading problem may have been associated with early brain injury.

The percentile scores of each of the 9 Retarded Readers are listed in Table 20. In order that these individual results can be compared with the group trend for Retarded Readers, the percentile equivalents of the means of the entire group of 39 Retarded Readers are also listed. Age, Verbal IQ, and Performance IQ, the first 3 entries of the table, were not converted to percentiles, since these measures are more meaningful in their original form.

INDIVIDUAL PROFILES OF
NINE RETARDED READERS

Subject 1: Severe Reading
Retardation, Left Handed

This boy was 14 years and 3 months of age at the time of testing. He had repeated the first grade and was in the 7th grade of a public school, but was not given ordinary grades in the majority of subjects. Despite several years of remedial training at the Reading Clinic of the public schools his reading had not progressed beyond Grade 1 level. His score of 1.2 on the Wide Range Achievement Test indicates an ability to read only the shortest and most common words such as "to," "see," and "cat." Essentially, then, the boy could be considered a nonreader.

The case history revealed no disorders during pregnancy or delivery except for possible mild jaundice at birth. The development of coordinative and language skills was reported as normal, with no significant childhood illnesses, accidents, or other problems except for a strabismus operation on both eyes at the age of 5.

At the time of testing the boy was said to have no problems of adjustment that were not directly related to his reading difficulty. He was well-behaved, active in sports and scouting with his peers, played the chord organ, and built plastic models. On the neurological examination he was adjudged to be normal except for a weakness of the left sternocleidomastoid muscle, probably in compensation for a mild residual strabismus.

The mother reported that she had difficulty in reading until the fourth grade, after being forced to change from the left hand to the right hand in writing in the first grade. A brother of the boy had reading difficulty, but was able to complete school after several years of special tutoring.

TABLE 20

Individual profiles of 9 retarded readers for selected measures, expressed in terms of percentiles of the Normal Reader group. Group means for the entire Retarded Reader group are also expressed as percentiles of the Normal Reader Group.

| Measure | No. | Subject Number | | | | | | | | | All Retarded Readers |
		1	2	3	4	5	6	7	8	9	
Age		14	14	14	10	10	13	14	14	14	13
Read. Achieve. (yrs.)	1	1.2	1.4	5.3	1.6	2.3	4.7	6.4	4.3	5.6	3.5
Verbal IQ	4	76	81	86	92	89	92	77	70	100	87
Performance IQ	5	98	107	107	122	129	95	101	97	107	107

PERCENTILE SCORES

Wechsler–Bellevue Subtests

Measure	No.	1	2	3	4	5	6	7	8	9	All Retarded Readers
Information	8	3	6	6	1	1	3	1	1	28	5
Comprehension	9	65	27	42	1	1	42	27	1	65	29
Digit Span	10	10	10	10	1	10	71	29	51	71	26
Arithmetic	11	0	32	32	0	0	32	18	0	55	9
Similarities	12	8	0	8	26	0	0	0	0	8	5
Vocabulary	13	81	22	44	0	0	0	44	6	44	16
Object Assem.	17	96	78	60	50	100	50	100	78	96	63
Digit Symbol	18	9	9	81	0	24	9	9	24	81	28

Other Measures from Indiana Neuropsychology Laboratory

Measure	No.	1	2	3	4	5	6	7	8	9	All Retarded Readers
Trail Making	19,20	0	23	76	0	5	10	44	8	94	8
Seashore Rhythm	27	3	8	8	0	8	38	21	74	38	5
Tact. Performance, preferred	22	59	85	83	96	95	24	83	59	95	79
Peabody Pic. Vocab., oral	33	61	59	41	4	0	1	82	33	54	33

Measures from Minnesota Aphasia Test

Measure	No.	1	2	3	4	5	6	7	8	9	All Retarded Readers
Sentence Repet.	60	21	4	21	21	4	21	44	44	67	25
Articulation	68	10	10	10	0	1	38	79	0	79	7
Serial Responses (Mos.)	70	0	0	6	0	0	59	13	3	59	1
Word Rhyming	73	0	0	0	0	0	0	0	31	1	0
Draw Man	80	22	83	13	5	9	13	62	17	31	17

Other Measures

Measure	No.	1	2	3	4	5	6	7	8	9	All Retarded Readers
Perceptual Speed	91–103	0	2	90	2	0	3	15	18	27	5
Spatial Orientation	104	18	24	13	13	88	35	35	54	54	26
Reversals	105	4	86	86	5	32	8	24	41	41	8
Visual Memory	108,109	0	60	8	0	37	1	15	24	99	8

Although nominally left handed, the boy showed relatively superior skill with the right hand in placing blocks in a form board (Tactual Performance Test), tapping speed, and strength of grip. On all remaining lateral dominance tasks, however, he showed consistent preference for the left hand, eye, and foot, and wrote his name more rapidly with the left hand.

He was unable to perform any tasks which involved reading or writing even the simplest words, and made many errors in identifying and writing letters and numbers. In writing numbers, both the 7 and the 9 were reversed, and all attempts at writing were in the form of printing rather than cursive script. Among the children tested, none had greater difficulty in reading, spelling, and writing than this boy.

Table 17 shows that the Verbal IQ of Subject 1 was more than 20 points below his normal Performance IQ of 98. However, his ability on the Verbal subtests was not uniformly poor. On both the Comprehension and Vocabulary subtests his percentile scores exceeded 50, indicating that he scored above the average for Normal Readers. On the remaining 4 Verbal subtests, which represented more highly structured verbal tasks, his scores were very low. On the 2 Performance subtests that were included in this analysis his scores conformed to those of other Retarded Readers, with a relatively good score in Object Assembly and a poor score on the Digit Symbol Test.

For 3 of the 4 other measures selected from the Neuropsychology Battery his scores conformed to the trend of Retarded Readers, with relatively poor scores on the Trail Making and Rhythm Tests and an above-average score on the Tactual Performance Test with the preferred hand. His relatively good score on the Peabody Picture Vocabulary Test supported the findings of the Wechsler Bellevue Vocabulary subtest in suggesting normalcy of general spoken language abilities.

On the 5 measures selected from the Minnesota Aphasia Test, the pattern of deficiency shown by Subject 1 did not differ from the general trend of Retarded Readers, who had extremely poor ability in naming days and months (Measure 70). Subject 1 reversed the order of the days Tuesday and Wednesday, named only two months — August and September — in correct consecutive sequence, and was unable to give any correct rhymes. His performance was also relatively poor in repeating sentences, in the articulation of simple words and phrases, and in drawing a man.

On the remaining 4 tests his scores were even poorer than those of the Retarded Readers as a whole. In the visual perceptual speed tests he was able to discriminate only about half as many items as the average Normal Reader within the allotted time, and he made almost 3 times as many errors as the average Normal Reader on the tests of visual memory.

This severely retarded reader conformed to the average pattern of Retarded Readers in showing severe deficiencies of certain verbal, visual, and visual perceptual speed abilities along with an above average proficiency in certain manipulative skills. He differed from the average Retarded Reader in showing no deficiencies of spoken vocabulary and verbal comprehension skills, and might in this sense be considered a "perceptual type" of specific reading disability.

Subject 2: Severe Reading Retardation

Subject 2, a 14 year old right-handed boy, was almost as severely retarded in reading as Subject 1. He had repeated the first grade because of illness and was making poor grades in the eighth grade of a public school at the time of testing. He was in his second year of remedial reading in the Reading Clinic of the public schools and was said to be making some progress in acquiring reading skills. However, his reading ability was barely superior to that of Subject 1.

No disorders of pregnancy, delivery, or early development were reported, except that he did not begin to talk until age 3, from which point he was said to progress normally in language development. At age 4 he had a high fever of unknown origin which lasted for several days, and some illness apparently associated with the fever kept him out of school during a large part of the first grade. The family physician reportedly diagnosed this illness as "sinus condition," and it did not recur thereafter. No further developmental difficulties were reported.

At the time of testing, Subject 2 was active in sports and in scouting with his peers, and was normal in all aspects of adjustment except for self-consciousness about his reading problem. The neurological examination was normal except for marked right-left confusion.

The father had both speech and reading difficulty and was given special speech and reading training. After completing grade school at age 15 he continued to have difficulty in spelling but was able to read books, magazines, and newspapers with no difficulty.

On tasks which involved the use of each hand separately, Subject 2 showed a normal pattern of right-hand superiority, and consistently preferred the right hand and foot on lateral dominance tests. However, on the visual dominance test (Measure 52) there was almost equal preference for the right eye and the left eye.

Whereas Subject 1 was almost totally incapable of performing reading, writing, or spelling tasks, Subject 2 was able to make a somewhat more organized attack, but he still did not exceed first or second-grade level on any task. He made no errors in writing letters or numbers, but did confuse "F" with "H" in identifying printed letters.

For the measures shown in Table 17, Subject 2 had a typical discrepancy of Verbal and Performance IQ, with no striking deviation from the average deficiencies of Retarded Readers on the Verbal subtests and the Digit Symbol Test, coupled with a good score on the Object Assembly Test. His scores on the remaining Neuropsychology Tests also followed the average trend, except for an above-average score on the Peabody Vocabulary Test. The expected deficiencies occurred in the verbal tasks from the Minnesota Aphasia Test, including

9 errors in naming months and only 10 of a possible 20 word rhymes given. However, his high score on the drawing of a man indicated adequacy in this nonverbal skill. For the remaining 4 measures, the Visual Perceptual Speed and Spatial Orientation tasks were performed at the expected level of deficiency, but he did score well above average on the 2 final measures, both of which were visual discrimination tasks with no speed of response component.

Subject 2, then, was a severely retarded reader who conformed to the average trend of deficiency in verbal abilities and in visual perceptual speed, but who was not deficient in certain visual discrimination tasks which did not require a rapid response. Relative to the hypothetical typologies described in a preceding section, he might be considered a "mixed perceptual-language type," but- with less widespread visual involvement than Subject 1.

Subject 3: Possible Hereditary Reading Disability

The father of Subject 3 had a history of reading difficulty strongly suggestive of reading disability. He had been classified as a mirror reader and had attended 2 special reading clinics. He had not completed high school until the age of 21 and had remained "slow" in reading and spelling. However, he had made a very successful vocational adjustment as a sales executive in a well-established firm.

Subject 3 was a breech birth, with no other complications of the prenatal, neonatal, or early childhood periods. His reading difficulty was noted when he began first grade, and he had several years of remedial training. After having repeated a grade, he was in Grade 8 at the time of testing, where his grades were reported as average. His reading ability was much superior to that of Subjects 1 and 2, but he was still retarded by over 4 years in relation to the age at which he began first grade. He was active in many sports and seemed to be normal in all aspects of adjustment other than problems directly resulting from his reading difficulty. The neurological examination was normal, with the neurologist reporting an impression of good neurological status.

For the measures shown in Table 17, the Verbal IQ and Performance IQ of Subject 3 coincided almost exactly with the average for Retarded Readers. On Verbal subtests, only his scores on the Comprehension and Vocabulary subtests approached the average of Normal Readers. On the Digit Symbol Test he scored well above average, thus reversing the usual trend for Retarded Readers. He also scored well above average on the other 2 measures that required visual perceptual speed — the Trail Making Test and the Visual Perceptual Speed Test. The only remaining score which deviated from the average trend for Retarded Readers was the Thurstone Reversals Test, where he obtained an above-average score.

In this subject, where there was a substantial probability of in-herited reading disability, the most pronounced deviation from the average pattern of Retarded Readers was an absence of deficiency on skills which required speed of response to complex visual stimuli. He would thus be classified as a "language type" of reading disability.

Subject 4: Possible Hereditary
Reading Disability

The father of Subject 4 had experienced a great deal of difficulty in learning to read and had not progressed beyond the eighth grade. De-spite a continued reading problem he became quite successful in op-erating his own contracting business. For this reason he could proba-bly be classified as having reading disability.

There were no unusual complications of pregnancy or delivery of Subject 4, and his early development was reported as normal. He was said to have stuttered at age 2, and again at age 6, when he was given speech therapy at school. At age 6, he had a severe case of chickenpox, accompanied by a very high fever. He was said to be unusually sensi-tive to family difficulties.

At the time of testing he had made very little progress in learning to read despite intensive remedial training at a private reading clinic. He was in Grade 4, and had repeated no grades, but was not graded in an ordinary manner. He was unusually proficient in certain aspects of motor coordination. He participated in Little League baseball, drove junior sports cars, and built models. The neurological examination was normal.

With regard to the measures shown in Table 17, Subject 4 was considerably above the average of Retarded Readers in Performance IQ. The interpretation of his percentile scores is somewhat compli-cated because he was one of the youngest subjects. However, on all measures in which Retarded Readers were deficient except the Simi-larities test, his scores were below the average for Retarded Readers. For the measures on which Retarded Readers were superior to Normal Readers, his performance was average on the Object Assembly Test and well above average on the Tactual Performance Test.

This boy, whose reading disability may have been hereditary, showed all of the verbal and visual deficiencies of the average Re-tarded Reader despite his high Performance IQ and his proficiency in recreational activities.

Subject 5: Reading Retardation
with High Performance IQ

This subject was selected for individual analysis because his Per-formance IQ of 129 was the highest among Retarded Readers. Like Subject 4, he was one of the younger Retarded Readers. His reading ability, while superior to that of subjects 1, 2, and 4, extended no further than the reading and spelling of a few very simple words. Since his father and brother had reading difficulty, he might also have been classified as a possible hereditary reading disability.

There were no unusual complications of pregnancy or delivery. The only difficulty of early development was a lisp. At the age of 6 months he had an ear infection which was said to have reduced his hearing. The hearing was reportedly restored after his ears had been lanced and his adenoids removed. At 7 years of age he fell from a wooden race car on a hill, struck his head, and was unconscious for a "short time." The attending physician diagnosed this as a slight concussion, and there were no aftereffects.

The father was said to read everything slowly. An older brother had received remedial reading and had apparently achieved a normal reading level. No other reading problems were reported on either side of the family. At the time of testing, Subject 5 was in Grade 4, where he received poor grades in all subjects except music, art, and physical education. Vision, hearing, speech, and general health were normal. The neurological examination was normal. He was active in scouts, the YMCA, sports, made model airplanes, and was said to complete paint-by-the-numbers paintings very skillfully. His relations with peers were no better than fair, and he demanded considerable attention from his parents.

The Performance IQ of 129 for Subject 5 was 50 points higher than his Verbal IQ. A uniform deficiency was shown on the Verbal subtests, with an excellent Object Assembly score and a poor Digit Symbol score. The Tactual Performance Test was performed very well, and he showed the expected deficiency on all of the remaining tasks except Spatial Orientation, although the Reversals and Visual Memory tests were probably near normal for a 10 year old.

This child, then, served as a good example of poor reading ability coupled with superior nonverbal intelligence. His reading retardation was accompanied by the characteristically severe deficiency of visual and verbal skills with the possible exception of visual tasks which did not require a rapid response, and his spatial orientation ability was well above average for a child of his age. This demonstrates that a joint visual and verbal impairment may be associated with reading disability even when other nonverbal abilities are well above average.

Subject 6: Reading Retardation with Near Equality of Verbal and Performance IQ

In contrast to the average discrepancy of 20 points between Verbal and Performance IQ for Retarded Readers as a group, this boy had a Verbal IQ of 92 and a Performance IQ of 95. It was of interest to determine whether a Retarded Reader with apparent uniformity of verbal and nonverbal intelligence would show the characteristic pattern of visual-verbal deficiency.

Although this 13 year old boy was retarded by well over 3 years in reading achievement and by 5 years in spelling achievement, his reading impairment was not nearly as severe as that of Subject 1 or Subject 2. He was able to read and write simple sentences with relatively few errors, and on the 2 forms of the Peabody Vocabulary Test he obtained exactly the same score for the spoken and written presentation of stimulus words. It should be further noted in this regard that his listening vocabulary IQ was 84 on the oral form of the Peabody Test. Although Subject 6 was definitely retarded in reading, he had attained a usable level of proficiency in reading and spelling skills.

The child was delivered about $3\frac{1}{2}$ weeks early and weighed 5 lbs. 2 oz. He was kept in an incubator for three weeks because of a loss of birth weight to below 5 lbs. Otherwise there were no complications of pregnancy or delivery, and early development was normal. The only marked difficulties reported were a very severe case of measles with an associated throat infection, and an apparent hypersensitivity of the skin to poison ivy and athlete's foot. No familial reading disability was reported.

At the time of testing, the boy was in Grade 6, having repeated Grade 1. He was making poor grades in reading and spelling, but making passing grades in other subjects. Vision, hearing, speech, and general health were normal; he engaged in scouting, YMCA, and church activities; and he earned money by mowing lawns and by delivering newspapers. There were no problems of peer adjustment and no family problems. The neurological examination was normal except for right-left confusion. On the lateral dominance examination Subject 6 was nominally right handed, and there was consistent preference for the right hand, foot, and eye. The relative superiority of the right hand was demonstrated on the Tactual Performance, Tapping, Strength of Grip, and Speed of Writing tests.

Although the Verbal and Performance IQ scores suggested a uniformity of intellectual abilities, there was considerable variation among subtests. Information, Similarities, Vocabulary, and Digit Symbol were poor, with Comprehension, Digit Span, Arithmetic, and Object Assembly closer to normal. Among the remaining tests the poorest performances were on all visual tasks, and on Oral Vocabulary and Rhyming. The Tactual Performance Test was also performed at a below-average level.

Subject 6 probably represents a child whose reading status is marginal in relation to his overall intellectual abilities. He could be classified either as a retarded reader who is also somewhat below normal in other abilities or as a dull-normal child with pronounced reading difficulty. His near equality of Verbal and Performance IQ is indicative of this borderline status. It is interesting to contrast the scores of Subject 6 to those of Subject 5. The high Performance IQ of Subject 5 is accompanied by a much more pronounced visual-verbal deficiency. This suggests that when reading disability occurs in conjunction with superior nonverbal IQ there tends to be a consistent deficiency of the visual and verbal skills associated with reading.

Subjects 7 and 8: Fraternal Twins
with Reading Disability

Both of these 14 year old, right-handed fraternal twins fulfilled the criteria of specific reading disability. Subject 7 was retarded in reading achievement by 2.9 years; Subject 8 by 4.9 years. This meant that one read at the level of a normal 11 year old and the other at the level of a normal 9 year old. This level was maintained in the majority of reading and spelling performances that were assessed, with Subject 7 capable of reading and writing relatively complex sentences and brief passages, and Subject 8 capable of reading and writing simple sentences with few errors.

The children were delivered three weeks early. Subject 7 weighed $5\frac{1}{2}$ lbs. and Subject 8 weighed $4\frac{1}{2}$ lbs. Neither was placed in an incubator. There were no other complications of pregnancy or delivery. Subject 7 was born with a cleft palate which was successfully repaired by an operation at age 2. Early development was normal. Subject 7 held up his head, sat up, crawled, and walked at earlier ages than his brother, who was much heavier. Both boys developed language at about the same rate, with Subject 7 having some initial difficulty because of his cleft palate. There were no unusual illnesses or injuries except that Subject 7 contracted rheumatic fever at age 11. This lasted about one year, with no aftereffects. There were no other siblings. Neither parent had had reading difficulty, and there was no family history of reading difficulty.

At the time of testing both boys were normal in vision and hearing. The speech of Subject 7 was normal, although the examiner noted poor voice quality associated with the repaired cleft palate; and Subject 8 had mild articulation difficulty. Subject 7 participated in sports and built models. Subject 8, who tended to be more passive, was interested in working with radios. The boys did not play together very much, but did play with the same group of boys. Both were adjudged normal in home adjustment, although Subject 8 gave some evidence of feelings of inferiority with respect to his more aggressive brother. Neurological examination for Subject 7 was negative except for mild right-left disorientation; mild right-left confusion was also noted for Subject 8, along with a café au lait spot on the lateral aspect of the right leg.

Both boys were in Grade 7 at the time of testing. Subject 8 received failing grades in all subjects, and Subject 7 received average to failing grades. Subject 8 had always had much more difficulty in reading and in all other school subjects than his twin.

Both boys were right handed. Both showed consistent preference for the right hand, eyes, and foot on lateral dominance test, and consistent superiority of the right hand on tests of lateralized skill.

The discrepancy between Verbal and Performance IQ was quite large for both boys, with Verbal IQ especially low in Subject 8. They were not too similar in the pattern of subtest scores. Subject 7 obtained particularly poor scores on the Information, Similarities, and

Digit Symbol subtest, and scored very high on the Object Assembly Test. Subject 8 performed very poorly on all Verbal subtests except Digit Span, and conformed to the average for Retarded Readers in Object Assembly and Digit Symbol.

On the remaining tests the twins differed markedly. Subject 7 scored above the average for Retarded Readers on all tests except Rhyming. Subject 8 scored at or below the average for Retarded Readers on Trail Making, Peabody Oral Vocabulary, Articulation, Naming Days and Months, and Draw a Man, but surpassed his twin by a considerable margin on Seashore Rhythm, Rhyming, Spatial Orientation, and Thurstone Reversals.

These twins met all criteria for reading disability, with one showing a much greater reading retardation. Their test performance was similar only in the relatively gross measures of Verbal and Performance IQ. Subject 7 performed many of the visual and verbal tasks quite well, but was surpassed by his brother on several other visual and verbal tasks. When specific reading disability occurred in close siblings, then, no distinct "types" of associated deficit occurred.

Subject 9: Retarded Reader with
Possible Acquired Brain Injury

This 14 year old Retarded Reader was of particular interest because he had sustained a fractured skull at age 4. The attending physician had reported to the mother that the "speech area" was affected. He was retarded in reading by about 4 years, and fell between Subjects 7 and 8 in his general ability on reading and spelling tasks.

Unfortunately, Subject 9 was the only child in the Retarded Reading Group for whom a complete case history could not be obtained.

At the time of testing the boy was in Grade 8, and appeared to be exceptionally mature and self-sufficient for his age. The neurological examination revealed that his right shoulder was slightly lower in position, with less associated arm swing on the right. There was also mild right-left disorientation. The rest of the examination was negative.

Subject 9 was nominally right handed, and showed consistent preference for the right hand and foot on lateral dominance tests. The left eye was found to be dominant on the ABC Vision Test. Superior skill with the right hand was shown on all tests involving lateralized skill.

The discrepancy between Verbal and Performance IQ was not large. The Verbal IQ of 100 was high relative to the mean of 87 for Retarded Readers, with the Performance IQ of 107 being exactly at the mean. The Verbal subtest scores, although elevated, followed the trend for Retarded Readers, with the lowest scores obtained on Information and Similarities. A relatively high score was also obtained on the Digit Symbol subtest. This finding, coupled with a high score on the Trail Making Test, suggested normal functioning in certain aspects of visual perceptual speed. However, the relatively low score on the Visual Perceptual Speed Test did demonstrate difficulty in this respect.

The only really poor score on the remaining tests was on the Rhyming Test. In a subject with a history of possible brain injury affecting the speech area, then, the overall test performance tended to be relatively good, with pronounced deficits occurring on only a few of the tests for which Retarded Readers as a group were severely deficient. If brain injury had occurred, its sequelae were relatively subtle and confined to reading, spelling, and a small number of visual and verbal skills. In some sense, this case, of the 9 cases considered here, may have come closest to a "specific" reading disability accompanied by very specific deficits of sequential processing.

DISCUSSION

Group analyses indicated a uniformity of associated nonreading deficit among Retarded Readers, but there were certain differences among the nine Retarded Readers who were selected for individual examination. In terms of the hypothetical classification scheme discussed at the beginning of this chapter, Subjects 1 and 7 could be categorized as perceptual reading disorders, since they attained a normal level of skill on certain language tasks in which Retarded Readers as a group were severely deficient. Subject 3 could be classified as a language type, since he scored within the normal range on almost all of the visual tasks, including visual perceptual speed, for which Retarded Readers as a group were severely deficient. Subjects 2 and 5 might be classified as mixed types, but with less widespread visual involvement, since they approached normal on 2 visual discrimination tasks which did not involve perceptual speed. Subjects 4, 6, and 8 would all fall into some sort of mixed category. And Subject 9 might be considered to have a quite specific disability, possibly restricted to sequential processing skills.

Although the individual differences among Retarded Readers were far from clear-cut, it is instructive to examine these differences in relation to the findings of previous group analyses. Table 21 indicates the standing of the nine Retarded Readers in relation to Normal Readers for the first 4 measures selected by multiple stepwise regression analysis. All 9 were well below normal in rhyming, and all but one were well below normal in visual perceptual speed for single forms. However, 4 were at or above normal in speaking vocabulary, and 5 were average or above average in the discrimination of reversed figures.

It will be recalled that although the rhyming test and the visual perceptual speed tests were highly correlated with the reading-spelling factor found for Retarded Readers, speaking vocabulary and discrimination of reversed figures were not; also, that the Retarded Readers were severely deficient on all 4 measures in the test-by-test comparisons. The trends observed in individual Retarded Readers, then, are

TABLE 21

Comparison of the 9 individual Retarded Readers on the 4 Nonreading Measures which best differentiated Retarded Readers from Normal Readers. The designation (-) indicates that the subject performed well below the average of Normal Readers relative to his Age; (0) indicates an approximation to average normal performance; and (+) indicates performance better than the average of Normal Readers relative to age.

	VERBAL		VISUAL	
Description of Subject	Rhyming (73)	Vocabulary (13)	Perceptual Speed (92)	Reversed Figures (105)
1. Severe read. retard.	-	+	-	-
2. Severe read. retard.	-	-	-	+
3. Poss. hereditary reading disability	-	0	+	+
4. Poss. hereditary reading disability	-	-	-	-
5. High Performance IQ	-	-	-	0
6. Small diff. between Verbal and Perf. IQ	-	-	-	-
7. Fraternal twin	-	0	-	-
8. Fraternal twin	-	-	-	0
9. Possible acquired brain injury	-	0	-	0

in accordance with the explanation of reading disability proposed at the end of Chapter 9. For the present group of Retarded Readers, relatively specific deficiencies of certain skills classified as sequential processing abilities were intrinsically associated with reading disability, and may well have directly imposed a limit upon reading acquisition. The deficiency of central processing seemed to be most clearly reflected on the Rhyming Test and, with some exceptions, on tests which required rapid responses to sequences of visual figures. The Retarded Readers were also deficient on other visual and verbal tasks which did not require this type of sequential processing, but they were sufficiently proficient in these skills so that the deficiencies did not directly limit the early stages of reading acquisition.

In terms of the above explanation, Retarded Readers could conceivably be placed in several different categories. There could be a perceptual type in which the basic difficulty in sequential processing was accompanied by other visual deficits but not by other verbal deficits; a language type in which the sequential processing difficulty was accompanied by verbal but not visual deficit; and a mixed type with both visual and verbal accompaniments to sequential processing difficulty. It is proposed that all types share the same basic deficit of sequential processing. However, it is recognized that an associated language impairment would impose direct limitations upon reading if a Retarded Reader were able to progress beyond the beginning stages of reading acquisition.

The 9 Retarded Readers were selected on the basis of certain characteristics that could have influenced the patterns of nonreading impairment. These characteristics were severity of reading impairment, possible hereditary factors, high Performance IQ, near equality of Verbal and Performance IQ, comparison of siblings, and possible early brain injury. There were no obviously unique patterns of nonreading impairment associated with any of these conditions. All seemed to involve some variation of the basic pattern of impairment. This suggests that reading difficulty could have resulted from a number of different conditions, including inheritance, prenatal or perinatal disorders, or early brain injury, but with all having one result in common — an impairment of sequential processing abilities.

It must be concluded that there were no completely distinct individual differences within the sample of Retarded Readers of the type in which reading disability would be associated with deficits of one class of nonreading skill in a given case and with a completely different set of nonreading skills in another case. The individual differences which did occur took the form of variations in the amount and type of nonreading impairment that accompanied the seemingly basic impairment of sequential processing abilities.

CHAPTER ELEVEN

Discussion of the Study

A comprehensive survey of the reading and nonreading abilities of a carefully selected group of boys with specific reading disability and a carefully matched group of normal readers was reported on the foregoing pages. Areas of normal functioning were differentiated from areas of subnormality by a variety of analytic procedures in an attempt to describe the configuration of abilities associated with specific reading disability. It was hoped that the results of this study would contribute to a further understanding of the organization and development of human abilities, and would, in particular, help to resolve some of the conflicting explanations of the "causes" of reading disability.

Reading disability was found not to be an isolated disorder in the group of retarded readers who were tested in this study, but to be accompanied by widespread impairment of nonreading skills. The indisputable evidence that the disability of these children was not confined to reading suggests that a significant impairment of nonreading skills would be found in any child with specific reading disability to whom a sufficiently comprehensive set of tests was administered.

One definite conclusion to be drawn from this study, then, is that the term "specific" has been inappropriately applied if it is meant to indicate that all or even almost all of the skills not directly related to reading are at a normal level in children with specific reading disability. There are, however, at least 2 other senses in which reading disability might be considered specific. In the first, reading retardation occurs in a child of "otherwise normal intelligence;" in the second, reading acquisition is limited by deficiencies in a specific set of nonreading skills. These 2 aspects of specificity are considered in the following sections.

SPECIFIC READING DISABILITY
DEFINED BY NORMAL INTELLIGENCE

When reading disability is designated as specific, it is implied that some aspects of intellectual functioning are normal. Since verbal intelligence tests may involve skills directly related to reading ability, it is common practice to demonstrate the intellectual normality of a child with specific reading disability by the use of a nonverbal intelligence test. The criterion of intellectual normality in the present study was a Performance IQ score within or above the normal range. This seemed to provide an adequate means of differentiating children with specific reading disability from children whose reading disability was associated with more generalized intellectual subnormality.

No restrictions were placed on Verbal IQ in selecting Retarded Readers. The observed deficiencies of Verbal IQ among Retarded Readers were consistently large. If normal Verbal IQ had been included in the criterion of intellectual normality it would probably have been extremely difficult to assemble a group of adequate size. And it might have been impossible to assemble a group whose mean Verbal and Performance IQ were equal, since there was no case among the total sample of Retarded Readers tested where a Performance IQ of 90 or above was accompanied by an equal or larger Verbal IQ.

The consistently low Verbal IQ in Retarded Readers was not at all unexpected. A number of other investigators have reported similar findings, as discussed in Chapter 5. This did, however, require that the definition of specific reading disability be qualified by the stipulation that this disorder tends to occur in conjunction with deficiencies of certain abilities sampled by verbal intelligence tests.

An examination of the individual subtest scores of the Performance IQ scale raised a further problem of interpretation. The Retarded Readers were very much subnormal on one of the 5 Performance subtests. The conclusion was inescapable that the Retarded Readers were subnormal not only in reading ability and verbal intelligence, but also in at least one of the abilities used to estimate what might be called "other-than-verbal" intelligence.

To allow for possible deficiencies on nonverbal subtests of intelligence tests, then, the definition of specific reading disability must be further qualified by the stipulation that this disorder tends to occur in conjunction with deficiencies of a rather large proportion of the abilities sampled by an intelligence test. This further erosion of the usefulness of the concept of specificity leads inevitably to a consideration of the definition of intelligence.

There has been much written about the scientific status of the concept of intelligence. The writer has discussed this in connection with another special disability (Doehring, 1965). In the present instance the issues seem quite clear. If it is postulated that specific reading disability serves merely as a barrier to the emergence of a child's normal innate intelligence there is no need for further debate regarding the specificity of the disorder, since such a proposition cannot at present be verified or refuted. If, however, the term intelligence is used simply to denote an individual's average level of ability for an aggregate of skills, then a further consideration of the specificity of reading disability could have some value in increasing our understanding of this disorder.

Problems of Defining Intelligence

According to one popular viewpoint, intelligence is an innate, pre-determined mental capacity which ennobles or degrades all of an individual's intellectual activities throughout his lifetime. A common corollary of this belief is that when a special disability such as deafness or reading disability prevents or delays the emergence of an individual's true potential, his underlying mental capacity will remain in pure, untapped form.

There has been a great deal of controversy regarding such definitions of intelligence, along with a number of attempts to express the concept of a general or unitary intelligence in more acceptable scientific form. Although the majority of psychological theorists no longer accept the notion of a pure, native intelligence, there seems to be a continued implicit use of this concept, which in some instances is probably appropriate, in discribing the intellectual capacity of children with certain special handicaps. For example, the "gifted underachiever" can be described as a child who has not reached his full intellectual potential, and this serves to demonstrate that some children may be able to surpass normal educational achievement if they are put into more challenging teaching situations. Such a rationale is not applicable to the problem of reading disability, however, because the conventional teaching situation has proven to be too challenging at least in respect to reading.

The postulation of a "normal native intelligence" in specific reading disability does not appear useful because it tends to prevent a realistic evaluation of the disorder. The value of a theory is at least partly determined by the degree to which it promotes further inquiry. Where specificity of reading disability is defined by normal innate potential, there is no obvious direction for further inquiry.

Specific Reading Disability
as an Asymmetry of Talent

If the notion of intelligence as innate mental capacity is discarded, a more modest and useful definition can be considered. Although a single IQ score may serve as an adequate index of the overall intellectual level of a normal child, any such summary score would not adequately represent the uneven pattern of abilities associated with specific reading disability. A detailed description is required, which may be given in terms of a listing of the skills which fall below the normal range.

This approach makes it possible to include sensory, perceptual, and motor abilities along with intellectual abilities in describing the asymmetry of talent in retarded readers. Such a single listing, with no artificial distinction between the abilities assessed by IQ subtests and other classes of ability, should facilitate further inquiry into the conditions under which this disorder occurs.

It is proposed that the child with reading disability cannot be described in as simple a manner as we describe the normal reader. The abilities of the retarded reader must be listed in detail, and the interrelationships among disabilities must be specified. In such a case the continued use of the term "specific" could be very misleading if it were taken to indicate that a child with specific reading disability is normal in every respect except for his reading ability *per se*.

SPECIFICITY OF READING DISABILITY IN RELATION TO PERSONAL AND SOCIAL ADJUSTMENT

Thus far only the types of ability measured by tests have been discussed. On these tests the disability of Retarded Readers was quite widespread. One might wonder whether such a pattern of deficiency does not bear a closer resemblance to general intellectual subnormality than to the ability of normal children. Evidence to the contrary, subject to the reservations noted regarding interview data, came from interviews with parents and conversations with teachers. The Retarded Readers did not appear to differ from Normal Readers in any aspects of personal and social adjustment other than school achievement and those extracurricular activities which required reading.

The Retarded Readers would undoubtedly be found superior to mentally deficient children in personal and social adjustment skills, and this superiority should have an important bearing on their subsequent life adjustment. The majority of Retarded Readers should be capable of maintaining an independent livelihood as adults, whereas children classified as mentally deficient usually require some form of custodial supervision throughout life.

An assessment of everyday adaptive abilities could play an important part in the definition of reading disability. As suggested previously, standard techniques should be developed for quantitative description of personal and social adjustment variables, and these measures could be included in the listing of sensory, perceptual, motor, and intellectual abilities. The interview method employed in the present study would not be satisfactory for such a purpose.

The inclusion of estimates of adjustmental variables with other measures of ability could help to clarify an important issue raised by the results of the present study. Since the only disability which seems to directly affect the retarded reader's life adjustment is the reading disability *per se,* does the extensive nonreading impairment play an important part in his real-life adjustment? If, as suggested, the adjustmental variables could be quantified, then the interrelationships of these measures with test scores could be evaluated by multiple correlational procedures in answering the above question. Such an ambitious undertaking would require a great deal of preliminary standardization, and goes well beyond the scope of the present study.

CONFIGURATION OF NONREADING IMPAIRMENT
IN RETARDED READERS

An attempt was made in the preceding sections to formulate a comprehensive and fully objective frame of reference for the description of specific reading disability. It is hoped that the usefulness of a common classification scheme for all relevant characteristics of retarded readers, including intelligence and personal/social adjustment variables, will be recognized. Our understanding of human abilities will be greatly advanced by the removal of artificial distinctions between these various modes of human functioning.

In addition to demonstrating the need for a comprehensive and objective description of retarded readers, the present results definitely indicated the types of nonreading ability which were most severely impaired. This observed configuration of impairment will be considered in relation to previous explanations of the origin of reading disability and to the patterns of impairment observed in adults with brain damage. Then the interrelationship of reading and nonreading impairment will be interpreted with reference to contemporary psychological theory.

Relation to Previous Explanations
of Reading Disability

The broad outlines of nonreading impairment seemed quite clear. The impairment, although somewhat diffuse, seemed to occur most consistently in visual nonverbal skills and in verbal nonvisual skills. There were significant deficiencies of some skills which involved neither visual nor verbal components, and a number of skills which did involve visual or verbal components were not significantly impaired. However, the trends were sufficiently marked to suggest that difficulty in reading, a term which encompasses all visual-verbal skills, occurred in conjunction with deficiencies of certain visual and verbal aptitudes. Within the hypothetical constellation of human abilities, the configuration of deficit of Retarded Readers was concentrated in certain regions of the visual dimension, in certain regions of the verbal dimension, and in the region of intersection of these two dimensions.

Such a probabilistic explanation of the focus of reading and nonreading impairment is hardly more than a restatement of the test results, but it could serve as a useful context for further inquiry. Among the obvious questions raised by this interpretation of results are: (1) Can reading disability occur in children with normal visual and verbal aptitudes? and (2) Do any children with combined visual and verbal impairment learn to read in a normal manner?

The very definite indication of relatively widespread visual and verbal impairment did not provide strong confirmation for any of the explanations of reading disability previously discussed in Chapters 1 and 5. Birch's (1962) suggestion of delayed perceptual maturation probably comes closest to fitting the present results, but includes no direct explanation of verbal deficit. If nonreading impairment had been restricted to a few specific types of skill, some of the previous explanations of reading disability might have been verified or refuted.

Although such supposed causes of reading disability as incomplete dominance, directional confusion, and Gestalt disturbances were not clearly associated with reading disability in the present study, these deficiencies may be quite apparent in younger retarded readers and then become less pronounced with increasing age. The present study involved assessment of the current status of older retarded readers, and negative findings with regard to certain factors do not rule out the possible importance of such factors in younger children with reading problems.

An objective procedure for describing the specificity of reading disability was proposed in the preceding sections. In the present section the configuration of observed impairment was characterized as a joint deficit of certain visual and verbal skills. Such a combination of poor aptitudes could conceivably result from any one of a number of conditions, including genetic transmission, disorders of pregnancy and delivery, or early brain injury. The limited examination of individual differences in the preceding chapter gave no indication that any particular pattern of nonreading deficit was uniquely related to any particular type of inherited or acquired pathology.

Relation to the Effects of Brain Lesions in Human Adults

Regardless of whether the poor visual and verbal aptitude in Retarded Readers might have resulted from hereditary factors, reproductive casualty, or neonatal disorders, it is reasonable to consider the possibility that some disturbance of brain functioning could be involved. A direct comparison with previous investigations of children with brain damage was not possible because such investigations have not been sufficiently broad in scope to permit an assessment of the required range of visual and verbal abilities (Benton, 1962). Instead, the pattern of impairment of Retarded Readers was assessed by comparison with patterns of impairment of adults with brain damage on the Indiana Neuropsychology Tests and the Minnesota Aphasia Test.

No striking resemblance to the effects of lateralized and nonlateralized brain damage was revealed by the test-by-test comparison of groups on the Neuropsychology Tests, including the modified Halstead-Wepman Aphasia Screening Test. However, the interpretive analyses of individual test results described in Chapter 7 did indicate a higher-than-normal incidence of probable cerebral dysfunction with a tendency toward left hemisphere involvement among Retarded Readers; and the pattern of impairment exhibited by Retarded Readers on the Minnesota Aphasia Test was similar to that of a class of patients with brain damage designated by Schuell, Jenkins, and Jimenez-Pabon (1964) as aphasia complicated by central involvement of visual processes. The joint visual-verbal disturbance in adult aphasic patients is thought to involve lesions in the posterior region of the left cerebral hemisphere, including adjacent regions of the temporal, parietal, and occipital areas.

While the suggestion of possible localized cerebral dysfunction is highly speculative, it does provide a reasonable basis for an explanation of the occurrence of a joint weakness in certain visual and verbal aptitudes. It must be emphasized, however, that there was no direct evidence of cerebral dysfunction in the Retarded Readers. Hence, the suggestion of a possible localized disturbance simply represents the most informed guess that could be made on the basis of the present results and reflects the assumption that some disturbance of cerebral function must be involved in reading disability.

The discussion of results began with the formulation of a rationale for the comprehensive evaluation of reading disability, then proceeded through a description of the most prominent characteristics of the observed nonreading deficit in the Retarded Readers to a hypothesis regarding the type of brain disturbance which might be involved in such a pattern of impairment. In the following section certain aspects of nonreading impairment which seemed most directly related to difficulty in reading acquisition are discussed with reference to several psychological theories.

FURTHER INTERPRETATION OF VISUAL VERBAL IMPAIRMENT IN READING DISABILITY

The original aims of this study — to determine the degree of specificity of reading disability and then to further determine whether the observed pattern of nonreading impairment corresponded to any previous explanation of the origin of specific reading disability — were accomplished, as reported on the preceding pages. As the analysis of data proceeded through the various stages reported in Chapters 5 through 10, a strong suggestion began to emerge that within the rather large group of verbal and visual tests on which the Retarded Readers were severely deficient a small subgroup of measures was most directly related to the reading problem. An interpretation of reading disability which fitted this finding was progressively developed, beginning with the interpretation of the factor analyses.

Certain types of visual and verbal deficit accompanying reading disability were said to be nonspecific in the sense that they were not highly correlated with a reading-spelling factor which emerged in the factor analysis for Retarded Readers. Some of the visual and verbal skills which did correlate highly with this factor within the group of Retarded Readers were also among the nonreading measures which contributed most to the differentiation between Retarded Readers and Normal Readers. It was suggested that this small set of visual and verbal tasks all required the sequential processing of related material. Reading obviously shares this requirement, and it was further inferred that reading disability in the present group of retarded readers could be explained in terms of a disorder of visual, verbal, and visual-verbal sequential processing.

The identification of a sequential processing deficiency as an intrinsic component of reading disability must be regarded as highly tentative, and may not apply to all forms of reading disability, but it does suggest a potentially useful direction for further inquiry.* Some of the theoretical implications of this explanation will be examined in relation to our current state of knowledge in psychology and neurology.

The tasks which were classified as involving sequential processing of related material required the subject to deal with a chain of associated events. On the tests which required visual perceptual speed the subject scanned a succession of nonverbal figures, numbers, or letters, and made a nonverbal underlining, connecting, or symbol-drawing response to indicate his successive identification of a particular visual stimulus within a series of related stimuli. On tests which required sequential verbal responding the only stimulus input was an initial instruction, and then the subject had to formulate and emit a succession of rhyming words or consecutive months. The common feature of these tasks was that all required successive responses to elemental components, with each component bearing some definite relationship to other components of the sequence. Moreover, the tasks were not necessarily regulated or paced by external stimulus input.

Sequential processing, as described, cannot be reduced to simple stimulus-response terms. The subject must "keep in mind" the characteristics of an entire sequence as he proceeds through the series of responses which complete a given task. The mechanics of reading obviously involve this type of activity. In fact, reading can be described as a sequential processing task which combines the visual requirements of perceptual speed tasks and the verbal requirements of sequential naming tasks.

The classification of specific reading disability as a sequential processing disorder can be further interpreted in relation to a number of theoretical explanations of human processing abilities, several of which are considered below.

Serial Order in Behavior

Lashley (1951) asserted that complex serial actions are especially characteristic of human behavior. He felt that serial actions could not be adequately described in terms of associative chains or chains of

---

*Kinsbourne and Warrington (1963) have used a very similar term, "sequential ordering," to describe the basic difficulty involved in one particular syndrome of reading disability.

reflexes in which each element in a series only affects the next element. A generalized pattern or schema of integration which determines the entire sequence must also be in operation. This schema is prepared at the time a sequence is initiated, and then some scanning mechanism is brought into play to regulate the sequence as it unfolds.

Lashley's discussion of serial order was formulated in terms of current neurological theory. Earlier theory had construed the central nervous system as being in a passive and generally quiescent state with only specific chains of reflexes active at any particular time, but contemporary theories postulate a dynamically organized, continuously active nervous system in which any input operates by interaction with the constant background excitation. All serial actions, then, must take place within "a great network of reverberatory circuits, constantly active" (Lashley, 1951, p. 131). In these terms, the sequential processing disorder of the retarded reader might be attributed to impairment of the schema of visual-verbal integration or to impairment of the scanning process. Or the difficulty could involve the mechanism by which the elements of a sequence are selected during scanning. This latter mechanism, stated Lashley, presented a real problem, to which he had no answer, in explaining serial order in behavior. As will be seen, other writers have also applied themselves to the explanation of serial order in behavior, but none have formulated the problem in more succinct terms than Lashley.

Sequential Action as a
Semiautonomous Process

The general rationale adopted by Lashley in discussing the problem of serial order was also used by Hebb (1949) in formulating a much more elaborate theory of behavioral organization. In his analysis of the central process which occurs in conjunction with the sensory and motor components of any behavioral event, Hebb postulated that central nervous system activity involves a complex interaction of mediating processes rather than straight-line transmission via neural reflex chains. These complex interactions take place according to a very orderly scheme. Central processes are said to consist of activity in closed loops formed by interconnections of nerve cells. These closed loops are called "cell assemblies." Cell assemblies are developed as a result of repeated stimulation during an organism's development.

The method by which cell assemblies are formed is fundamental to Hebb's theory, and he described this process in great detail. Briefly, cell assemblies are developed under the combined influence of repeated stimulation (environmental factors) and the inherited characteristics of the central nervous system (hereditary factors). The whole process is designated as perceptual learning.

Cell assemblies, once developed, can maintain their activity independently of sensory input, and can thus be regarded as the elements of central processing. Another fundamental postulate of Hebb's theory is that active cell assemblies can excite other cell assemblies. This may occur in the form of a series of excitations called a "phase sequence." The phase sequence can be regarded as a train of thought made up of a succession of elementary ideas or percepts which correspond to cell assemblies.

A final fundamental postulate of Hebb's theory relates to the direction of development and transmission of the phase sequences — the factor of selective attention in thinking. This is explained in terms of a summation of activity or "set" in which the activity in one cell assembly predisposes or "primes" the firing of other assemblies within a habitual phase sequence. This aspect of Hebb's theory was reformulated by P. Milner (1957) in the light of new neurophysiological findings regarding arousal and inhibition in brain functioning. According to Milner, the ease with which a given cell assembly can be activated during a train of thought or during associative learning depends jointly upon (1) the strength of the cell assembly, as determined by the amount of "perceptual overlearning" which has gone into the formation of the assembly, and (2) the current conditions of priming or set for that particular assembly.

The second factor specified by Milner can be considered the necessary context for selective activation. This context is determined by (1) the degree of similarity between present conditions and the conditions under which the assembly in question was previously activated, (2) the effectiveness with which competing cell assemblies are inhibited, and (3) the general state of arousal or wakefulness of the organism.

All of the factors described in the above paragraphs are operative in determining whether a given cell assembly is activated during a train of thought. These factors serve the same function during perceptual learning, during associative learning, in the formation of cell assemblies, and in the formation of phase sequences. The current train of thought might be said to merely represent the ongoing phase of a learning process that continues throughout the lifetime of the organism.

Hebb's theory seems singularly appropriate for the further interpretation of a possible impairment of sequential processing. If nothing more, the problem can be structured in more explicit terms by a consideration of whether a sequential processing disorder could involve a failure to achieve perceptual overlearning in the original formation of cell assemblies, a deficiency in the organization of the associative set in which a cell assembly is to be activated, a failure to inhibit competing neural processes, or a deficiency of general arousal. Hebb and Milner have made a very direct attempt to formulate a systematic explanation of the manner in which appropriate elements are selectively activated during sequential central processing. This is the issue which Lashley designated as the real problem of explaining serial order in behavior. If the crux of the retarded readers' difficulty in reading acquisition has something to do with a difficulty in the overlearning or the selective activation of visual verbal sequences, Hebb's theory provides a complex but well-marked path for further exploration.

Some additional comments regarding perceptual and cognitive organization in Hebb's later writing are also pertinent to the present discussion. In connection with the complexity of human learning he points out that random activity of nerve cells not directly required for learning can interfere with the learning process (Hebb, 1961a). This assertion is, of course, consistent with Milner's postulation of the necessity for inhibiting competing cell assemblies during the selective activation of a given assembly. Chronic malfunction of a particular cerebral region in retarded readers, as previously suggested by analogy with adult aphasics, could result in an abnormal amount of random nerve cell activity and thus selectively interfere with visual-verbal sequential processing.

Hebb (1963) also attempted to clarify the distinction between sensory and perceptual processes in the central nervous system. While configurations of excitation in primary sensory areas are directly representative of patterns of stimulation, perceptual processes can operate in a semiautonomous manner in relation to sensory input. These processes take place in the "divergent-conduction" areas of the brain, not in the primary sensory areas. Perceptual processes are influenced not only by current sensory input, but also by general contextual factors and by current trains of thought. This means that sequential processing during reading is not entirely under the control of the stimulus configuration. The processing of serially ordered stimuli can sometimes be successfully completed even when the stimulus is presented in reverse order, as in the mirror image of a printed word. This recalls Lashley's contention that serial order in behavior does not necessarily involve a unidirectional chain of conditioned reflexes. Thus, the gross deficiency of retarded readers on visual perceptual speed tasks does not necessarily result from an impairment of sensory processing in the primary visual area of the brain. Such a deficiency could result from an impairment of processing in a divergent conduction area in which visual and verbal sequences were jointly concerned. That such an explanation might be plausible is suggested by the finding that circumscribed lesions of the left temporal lobe may result in relatively subtle reading and listening difficulties described as a decrease in the ability to assimilate sequential verbal information (B. Milner, 1958).

As Hebb (1959) points out, his theory and other contemporary theories must be regarded as mere guidelines for further speculation. One of the more active areas of speculation in theoretical psychology relates to the role of expectancy or perceptual set in shaping human behavior. Setting factors were mentioned in the discussion of Hebb's theory and must be considered important for any further interpretation of a sequential processing disorder in retarded readers. Some of the ways in which setting factors have been treated in recent theories are considered briefly in the next section.

Plans, Models, and Response
Biases as Setting Factors

Bruner, Goodnow, and Austin (1956) suggested that the organism forms a "model" of its environment during perceptual development. As the model is formed, recurrent regularities of the environment are organized into discrete categories, and the organism then responds on the basis of these learned perceptual categories rather than responding to all discriminable details of the environment. In any situation where there is uncertainty regarding the exact nature of environmental input the perceptual categories may be applied as hypotheses. This can happen, for example, in the identification of an acquaintance at a distance. The application of hypotheses can play an important role in reading, as illustrated by the results of studies involving brief exposure of printed words (cf. Howes, 1954).

Miller, Galanter, and Pribram (1960) adopted the term "Plan" to describe the system by which an organism adapts to its environment. They were directly concerned with the inadequacy of the reflex arc as a unit of behavior, and proposed that behavior is mediated by plans rather than by more direct connection of stimulus and response. The Plan was said to be similar to a program which guides a computer in the sense that it controlled the order in which a sequence of operations was to be carried out. Although Miller, Galanter, and Pribram were not primarily concerned with the manner in which Plans are developed, an obvious analogy could be drawn between their Plans, Hebb's phase sequences, and Lashley's serial order phenomena. A prescribed sequence such as an instruction to rhyme words or to read a printed passage is processed by the execution of a Plan. The Plan functions as the schema of integration or phase sequence in controlling the order of sequential operations. A disorder of sequential processing could result from an immature Plan, an inappropriate Plan, or a generally inadequate collection of visual and verbal Plans.

A very rigorous explanation of the manner in which setting factors can influence perception has been derived from statistical decision theory. Goldiamond (1958) discussed the importance of "response bias" as a determinant of visual perception. Response bias can be built into an individual by systematic training procedures and could presumably operate at the neural level in the manner described by P. Milner (1957). A retarded reader, then, could have failed to develop an effective bias to respond in the reading situation.

Not all current theoretical formulations of possible relevance have been mentioned. For example, information theory (cf. Cherry, 1957) would undoubtedly prove to be an appropriate system for further interpretation of a sequential processing disorder. For the present, however, the point to be emphasized is that many contemporary theories would not explain sequential processing in terms of a unidirectional chain of actions. The processing of a sequential action involves a dynamic interaction of input, output, and central processes, all of which takes place in the context of organized background activity. A defect of a particular kind of processing skill can be analyzed by a systematic examination of the components of this interactive system. In Retarded Readers the input and output components *per se* seem normal, as do general components of arousal, motivation, and overall integrity of adjustmental processes. It must be assumed that the defect is restricted to certain centrally organized visual and verbal sequential processes. Some of the possible sources of such a central defect have been mentioned: defects of perceptual overlearning, of perceptual set (or Plans or hypotheses or response biases), or of the inhibition of irrelevant background activity.

As a final step in the interpretation of the present results it has been proposed that the reading disability of Retarded Readers was closely associated with a difficulty in the processing of certain visual, verbal, and visual-verbal sequences, and that this selective disturbance could be associated with chronic dysfunction somewhere near the conjunction of the temporal, parietal, and occipital areas of the left cerebral hemisphere. This final interpretation of the present study seems to bring us back to the concept of congenital word blindness originally proposed by Morgan and Hinshelwood, but with a certain amount of new theoretical window dressing.

RECOMMENDATIONS FOR FURTHER RESEARCH

It has been proposed that specific reading disability involves a difficulty in the processing of visual-verbal sequences, possibly as a result of congenital or early dysfunction of a particular region of the cerebral cortex. This explanation does not give anything approaching a final answer, as it intends simply to suggest a useful direction for further inquiry. As is the case with most investigations of this type, a partial replication using the most promising tests, a better case history procedure, and a larger sample more homogeneous with respect to age, are sorely needed to verify or refute the present findings. With regard to possible cerebral involvement, a further comparison of the configurations of impairment in children with specific reading disability, children with neurologically confirmed cerebral dysfunction, and adult aphasic patients with joint visual-verbal involvement could also be made. Also, sequential learning processes in retarded readers should be analyzed more intensively. For example, the abilities of retarded readers could be compared with normal readers in learning to read through nonvisual sensory channels (cf. Donaldson, 1965), in learning to read spatially transposed printed material (Kolers, Eden, and Boyer, 1964), and in cumulative learning of highly structured digit repetition tasks (Hebb, 1961a). Other sequential processing tasks should also suggest themselves as the exact form of the deficit in retarded readers becomes clearer.

There should be no suggestion, however, that the scope of investigation should be narrowed to focus on a single hypothetical explanation of reading disability. This disorder can be approached from a number of different aspects, all of which deserve fuller exploration. There are as many potential explanations of reading disability as there are ways in which different definitions of reading can be combined with different criteria of normal functioning in retarded readers. There is no particular reason at this time to regard specific reading disability as a single problem with a single cause.

The strongest recommendation with respect to further research is that full cognizance should be taken of current knowledge in the neurological and behavioral sciences. There have been major advances in these disciplines over the past 2 decades, and it should be clearly recognized that many of the well-known explanations of reading disability were based on what Hebb (1961b) described as seventeenth-century physiology and nineteenth-century psychology. The entire concept of reading disability should be periodically reviewed and revised in the light of new scientific knowledge.

In addition to the recommendations for more intensive analysis of a possible sequential processing disorder and for a continuing reexamination of the concept of reading disability, several other recommendations which evolved from analysis of the present study are presented below.

Further Cross-Sectional Investigations

The present study can be classified as a cross-sectional investigation of the current status of many abilities in retarded readers with 4 years or more of reading instruction. The value of a replication study for confirming the observed trends was mentioned above. Since an exact duplication of procedures is usually not advisable, partial replication studies could employ a refined set of measures and a more elaborate statistical analysis. The analysis of the results of a large battery of tests by a variety of statistical techniques proved to be very informative, and it must be assumed that more appropriate measures of ability and more appropriate statistical techniques would be available for future investigations.

In view of the knotty problems involved in the use of a nonverbal IQ score as an index of normal intellectual capacity in retarded readers, several suggestions regarding additional subject groupings in further studies have been made, including retarded readers with normal verbal intelligence, normal readers with low verbal and nonverbal intelligence, and barely normal readers with exceptionally high verbal and nonverbal intelligence. Other possibly informative groups might be normal readers with severe congenital hearing impairment, and normal readers with severe environmental deprivation.

Although the present study probably involved a larger number of tests than any previous investigation of reading disability, not all relevant classes of ability were thoroughly assessed. The severe impairment in the one nonverbal auditory test (the Rhythm Test) suggests that an auditory sequential processing disorder may have been found if non-verbal auditory abilities had been more thoroughly assessed. A more complete survey of auditory abilities might reveal whether subgroups of "audile" and "visile" retarded readers can be differentiated (Wepman, 1962). Likewise, the language development of retarded readers could be more thoroughly analyzed (cf. Myklebust, 1965).

Changes in Configuration of Nonreading
Impairment as a Function of Age

The pattern of nonreading impairment could be quite different in younger retarded readers. As Harris (1961) has pointed out, some forms of impairment which do not occur at all in older retarded readers may be directly related to reading difficulty in younger retarded readers. A series of cross-sectional comparisons of normal and retarded readers in several age groups or a longitudinal investigation of changes in patterns of disability in the same normal and retarded readers over a decade or so would provide a very important added dimension to the results of the present study. The major difficulties in carrying out such studies would relate to the early identification of reading disability in beginning readers and to the total effort and expense of carrying out either longitudinal or multiple cross-sectional studies. The present study, which was quite ambitious in the latter regard, would constitute only a small fraction of an adequate survey of changes in nonreading impairment as a function of age.

Relation of Reading Disability
to Methods of Teaching Reading

Reading disability is defined in part by the method or methods which have proven unsuccessful in teaching the retarded reader to read. This factor is explicitly recognized by the teacher who tries a wide variety of methods in dealing with retarded readers instead of putting all of her faith in one particular method. In addition to keeping informed of relevant scientific knowledge the investigator of reading disability should be aware of current educational research relating to the development and evaluation of methods for teaching reading. The entire problem of reading disability could change as new teaching methods are introduced. Where large-scale, carefully controlled comparisons of different teaching methods are made, it would be especially interesting to evaluate the patterns of nonreading impairment of "otherwise normal" children who fail to learn by each of the methods under comparison.

Research in Reading Acquisition

There has been a recent increase in research on certain aspects of reading acquisition. Several of these studies (Doehring and Lacy, 1962; Hively, 1964; Staats *et al.*, 1962) were concerned with the experimental analysis of early reading behavior by use of the type of systematic instructional procedures recommended by Skinner (1954). The purpose of such studies is to arrive at a precise description of the essential conditions for reading acquisition.

It is to be hoped that the results of such studies of reading acquisition will be directly pertinent to the results of cross-sectional investigations of patterns of impairment in retarded readers. Ferguson (1954) has emphasized the need for developing a common conceptual framework for studies of the learning process and studies of human ability. He proposed a generalized theory of learning and human ability which took into consideration the types of ability classified as intelligence, and the influence of biological and cultural factors in the development of abilities. An ability was considered to be the end-product of overlearning a task, and most learning beyond early infancy was said to involve a transfer of training from previously overlearned skills. Ferguson's emphasis upon the continuity of learning and human abilities is of obvious importance to a consideration of the mutual benefit to be derived from different approaches to the study of reading.

Gagné (1962) made a more explicit formulation of the manner in which abilities may be developed through what he called "productive learning." Productive learning is said to involve transfer from earlier learning sets to new skills which incorporate the previously acquired abilities. A hierarchy of knowledge develops by transfer of training from extremely simple levels, such as discriminations, through tasks of greater and greater degrees of complexity. The hierarchical acquisition of knowledge can, according to Gagné, be studied most effectively by the types of systematic instructional techniques that have been used in the investigations of early reading behavior cited above.

Research in beginning reading appears to suggest the same general direction for future research as did the results of the present investigation of patterns of nonreading impairment in children with reading disability. In our quest for further understanding of the factors which lead to success or failure in reading acquisition, particular attention must be paid to language and visual perceptual overlearning, to the acquisition of specific sequential processing skills, and to the development of perceptual and learning sets as a function of the previously acquired hierarchy of knowledge.

SIGNIFICANCE OF THE PROBLEM

The importance of further research into the problem of reading disability has been spelled out in some detail in relation to an increase in our understanding of human ability. The practical importance of further research for children who have such reading problems should also be obvious. Ideally, the retarded reader is diagnosed and tutored by the best methods available. Any further understanding of the implications of nonreading impairment should lead to an improvement of such procedures and should provide a more accurate prognosis for the child and his parents. New findings in this area should also suggest methods for decreasing the incidence of reading disability by revision of reading-readiness procedures and techniques for teaching beginning reading.

Reading is an ability of prime importance in our culture. Every effort should be made to provide as many children as possible with adequate conditions for learning to read. Our attempts to understand reading disability could lead to a significant reduction in the number of children whose educational opportunity is seriously curtailed by a failure to master the basic mechanics of reading.

CHAPTER TWELVE

Summary and Conclusions

This study was concerned with specific reading disability as defined by severe retardation of reading ability in children who did not otherwise seem to differ from normal readers. A comprehensive survey of the abilities of retarded readers was carried out. The primary aim was to delineate more precisely the specificity of reading disability in these children by determining what other abilities were subnormal and how these other disabilities might be related to reading disability. It was felt that such a study could provide useful information regarding the identification and training of children with specific reading disability, and should also contribute to a further understanding of the organization and development of human abilities.

A specific reading disability group was selected which consisted of 39 boys ranging in age from 10 through 14 who met the following criteria: retardation in oral reading ability by 2 years or more despite remedial reading instruction, a specific complaint regarding the reading problem, Wechsler-Bellevue Performance IQ of 90 or above, and normality of educational opportunity, psychiatric status, vision and hearing, general health, and home environment. This group was designated as Retarded Readers and was compared with a group of 39 boys and a group of 39 girls with oral reading achievement in the normal range and with no history of reading disability. Each of the latter groups was matched with the Retarded Readers in Age and Performance IQ and was comparable to the Retarded Readers with regard to the remaining variables listed above. The main data analyses involved a comparison of the Retarded Readers and the male normal readers, hereinafter designated as Normal Readers.

All subjects were given a series of tests derived, for the most part, from a test battery developed at the Indiana University Neuropsychology Laboratory for the evaluation of 10- to 14-year old children with suspected neurological disorders, and from the Minnesota Test for Differential Diagnosis of Aphasia. These tests, plus several additional psychological tests, yielded a total of 109 measures. The entire group of tests was intended to sample a wide variety of sensory, motor, perceptual, and verbal abilities which might be related to specific reading disability. In addition, all of the Retarded Readers and over half of the Normal Readers were given a neurological examination, and detailed case history information was obtained by interviews with all but a few of the children.

145

The test results were analyzed by several different statistical procedures. Analysis of covariance was used for a test-by-test comparison of Retarded Readers and Normal Readers. The interrelationships among reading and other abilities were explored by factor analysis; and two other multiple correlation procedures — multiple stepwise regression analysis and discriminant analysis — were used to determine what disabilities other than reading disability most clearly differentiated Retarded Readers and Normal Readers. The groups were compared with respect to neurological status by a blind evaluation of the reports of the neurological examination and the case history interview data, and the probability of cerebral dysfunction in individual Retarded Readers and Normal Readers was estimated by blind evaluation of the results of the Neuropsychology Tests. Finally, the test profiles of 9 of the Retarded Readers were examined in detail.

The test-by-test statistical comparisons revealed that the disability of Retarded Readers was not restricted to skills that required reading or spelling. The Normal Readers were significantly superior to Retarded Readers on 62 of the 103 measures that were statistically analyzed. The pattern of deficit was characterized as an interaction of visual and verbal impairment, involving both verbal and nonverbal visual skills and both visual and auditory verbal skills. This pattern was not entirely consistent, since there were many visual and verbal tasks on which the groups did not differ significantly, as well as a number of tasks with neither visual nor verbal requirements on which Retarded Readers were significantly deficient. The Retarded Readers were significantly superior to Normal Readers on several tasks with somesthetic input, a finding which could be interpreted as indicating retardation in perceptual maturation. The configuration of impairment on the Neuropsychology Tests did not conform to patterns of disability observed in adults with brain damage. Nor did the overall configuration of impairment provide strong support for any previous theoretical explanations of reading disability. However, the pattern of impairment of the Retarded Readers on the Minnesota Aphasia Test did resemble that of brain-damaged adults with aphasia complicated by central involvement of visual processes.

The analysis of neurological reports and case history information did not suggest any clear-cut predisposing conditions for reading disability other than a high incidence of directional confusion on the neurological examination. Despite the severe and widespread deficiency of Retarded Readers in both reading and nonreading skills, there was nothing in their medical or developmental history and nothing in reports of their current personal and social adjustment that markedly distinguished them from Normal Readers.

A significantly larger number of Retarded Readers were adjudged by the blind evaluations of the Neuropsychology Tests to have probable cerebral dysfunction with a marked tendency toward left hemisphere involvement. It was concluded that this form of analysis, in contrast to the test-by-test statistical comparisons, afforded a more sensitive procedure for assessing possible cerebral dysfunction because of the possibility of evaluating patterns of individual test results.

A separate factor analysis was calculated for each group, with a definite reading factor emerging as the major factor in each analysis. There were very pronounced differences between groups in the composition of this factor. Tests requiring visual and verbal sequential processing were highly correlated with the reading factor for Retarded Readers, and tests of oral vocabulary were highly correlated with the reading factor for Normal Readers. The similarity of the remaining factors suggested that there were no other gross differences between groups in the organization and integration of abilities.

The multiple stepwise regression analysis showed that apart from measures which required reading or spelling, 2 spoken language abilities — word rhyming and oral vocabulary — and 2 visual abilities — discrimination of reversed figures and visual perceptual speed for single forms — made the greatest unique contribution to the differentiation of Retarded Readers and Normal Readers. The discriminant analyses demonstrated that the 2 groups were as clearly separated by an optimal weighted score derived from these 4 measures as they were by the original criterion of oral reading achievement.

The detailed examination of the test profiles of nine Retarded Readers revealed certain individual differences. Two of the 9 Retarded Readers approached normality on verbal tasks, one approached normality on visual tasks, and one approached normality on almost all tasks that did not require reading. However, all were deficient on at least one nonreading task which required sequential processing.

An overall evaluation of these results suggested the following conclusions:

1. Reading disability in the present group of Retarded Readers was accompanied by impairment of a wide variety of skills which did not require reading; therefore, the term "specific" could not be appropriately applied to the description of the reading disorder.

2. The most consistent nonreading impairment occurred in certain types of visual tasks and in certain types of verbal tasks, although other visual and verbal tasks were performed at a normal level.

3. The reading disability of Retarded Readers was most highly correlated with visual and verbal tasks that required the sequential processing of related material.

The notion of "otherwise normal intelligence" as a necessary defining characteristic of specific reading disability was seriously questioned because Retarded Readers were found to be significantly deficient on all of the Verbal subtests and on one of the 5 Performance subtests of the Wechsler-Bellevue Scale, and because a concept of unitary native intelligence does not provide a useful basis for further inquiry. It was recommended that reading disability be defined instead in terms of a comprehensive and detailed listing of abilities, including perceptual, motor, and verbal skills, as well as quantified estimates of personal and social adjustment skills.

Although there was no direct evidence of neurological disturbance, the pattern of impairment exhibited by Retarded Readers could conceivably be associated with inadequate functioning of a circumscribed region in the posterior left cerebral cortex. Further comparison of the patterns of ability of retarded readers and adults with brain damage having combined visual and verbal impairment should provide valuable information in this regard.

The finding of a high correlation between certain tasks requiring sequential processing and oral reading achievement in Retarded Readers was interpreted in relation to several contemporary psychological theories, notably that of Hebb. It was concluded that the processing of a sequential action such as reading must involve a dynamic interaction of input, output, and central processes, all of which takes place in the context of highly organized background activity of the central nervous system. Defects of processing skills can be investigated by systematic analysis of the components of this interactional system. The importance of such factors as arousal and perceptual learning to the present problem was stressed. Further inquiry into reading disability should make use of current theories rather than relying on outmoded concepts of psychology and neurology.

The implications of the present study for future research were considered. The importance of determining how the pattern of disability changes as a function of age and as a function of variations in the criteria used for defining reading disability was pointed out, as was the necessity for direct continuity between research in reading disability and research into the process of reading acquisition.

Finally, the continuing importance of a further understanding of the circumstances under which some children are unable to acquire a basic human skill was emphasized.

APPENDICES A-E

Description of Tests

Measure no.

I   *Tests routinely administered to young patients referred to the Neuropsychology Laboratory, Indiana University Medical Center*

A.   WIDE RANGE ACHIEVEMENT TEST (Jastak, 1946).

1   READING. Standardized test of oral word reading achievement. *Score:* grade level based on total number of words correctly read aloud. *Task Requirement:* association of printed letters with spoken word. *Stimulus:* printed word. *Response:* spoken word. *This test was used as the criterion for reading achievement.*

2   SPELLING. Standardized test of written spelling achievement. *Score:* grade level based on total number of words correctly spelled. *Task Requirement:* written production of spoken word. *Stimulus:* spoken word. *Response:* written word.

B.   WECHSLER-BELLEVUE INTELLIGENCE SCALE, FORM 1 (Wechsler, 1944).

3   FULL SCALE IQ. Composite score derived from total weighted subtest scores. Indicative of overall intellectual functioning.

4   VERBAL IQ. Composite score derived from total weighted scores of the 5 Verbal subtests (excluding the Vocabulary test). Indicative of overall verbal functioning.

5   PERFORMANCE IQ. Composite score derived from total weighted scores of the 5 Performance subtests. Indicative of overall nonverbal functioning. *This measure was used as the criterion of nonverbal intelligence.*

6   VERBAL WEIGHTED SCORE. Total weighted scores of the 5 Verbal subtests before conversion to Verbal IQ.

7   PERFORMANCE WEIGHTED SCORE. Total weighted scores of the 5 performance subtests before conversion to Performance IQ.

Verbal subtests

8   INFORMATION. 25 questions. Assesses elementary factual knowledge of history, geography, current events, literature, and general science. *Score:* number of items correct. *Task Requirement:* retrieval of acquired verbal information. *Stimulus:* spoken question of fact. *Response:* spoken answer.

Measure no.

9   COMPREHENSION. 10 questions. Assesses the ability to evaluate certain situations. *Score:* number of items correct. *Task Requirement:* evaluation of verbally formulated problem situations. *Stimulus:* spoken question of opinion. *Response:* spoken answer.

10   MEMORY SPAN FOR DIGITS. Repetition in forward order of three- to nine-digit numbers and repetition in reversed order of two- to eight-digit numbers. *Score:* simple total of forward and reversed digit span. *Task Requirement:* short-term memory for digits. *Stimulus:* spoken numbers. *Response:* spoken numbers.

11   ARITHMETICAL REASONING. 10 arithmetic problems of increasing difficulty. *Score:* number of problems correctly solved, with time credit. *Task Requirement:* arithmetic reasoning. *Stimulus:* spoken (first 8 items) or printed (last 2 items) question. *Response:* spoken answer.

12   SIMILARITIES. 12 pairs of words. The most essential semantically common characteristic of word pairs must be stated. *Score:* number correct. *Task Requirement:* verbal abstraction. *Stimulus:* spoken question. *Response:* spoken answer.

13   VOCABULARY. (not included in Verbal IQ or Verbal Weighted Score) 42 words. Spoken definition of words. *Score:* number words correct. *Task Requirement:* verbal definition. *Stimulus:* spoken word. *Response:* spoken definition.

Performance subtests

14   PICTURE ARRANGEMENT. 6 series of picture cards. Pictures are sequentially arranged to form story. *Score:* total credits for speed and accuracy of arrangement. *Task Requirement:* manipulation of the order of picture cards to form the most probable sequence of events. *Stimulus:* pictures. *Response:* simple motor manipulation.

15   PICTURE COMPLETION. 15 pictures of familiar objects, each with a part missing. The missing part is identified in simple line drawings. *Score:* number of missing parts correctly identified. *Task Requirement:* location of missing part on the basis of memory of the whole object. *Stimulus:* picture. *Response:* spoken name of missing part.

16   BLOCK DESIGN. 7 designs. Arrangement of colored blocks to form designs which match those on printed cards. *Score:* total score for speed and accuracy of block placement. *Task Requirement:* arrangement of blocks to match a printed design. *Stimulus:* printed geometric design. *Response:* manipulation and arrangement of blocks.

17   OBJECT ASSEMBLY. 3 formboards. Parts of each formboard are to be arranged to form a picture. *Score:* total score for speed and accuracy of assembly. *Task Requirement:* spatial arrangement of parts to form a meaningful whole. *Stimulus:* disarranged parts of picture. *Response:* complex manipulation and arrangement of parts.

18   DIGIT SYMBOL. 67 digits, preceded by a code which relates digits to symbols. Symbols are to be written below digits as rapidly as possible. *Score:* number of symbols correctly written within a fixed time. *Task Requirement:* association of digits and symbols by direct visual identification or by short-term memorization. *Stimulus:* printed digits and symbols. *Response:* rapid coordination of visual identification with a complex writing response.

Measure no.

C.   TRAIL MAKING TEST (Reitan, 1958).

19   PART A. 25 numbered circles are distributed over a sheet of paper. The circles are connected by a pencil line in the correct sequence. *Score:* time to complete. *Task Requirement:* sequential identification of numbers. *Stimulus:* spatially disarranged printed numbers. *Response:* rapid coordination of visual identification with a simple motor response.

20   PART B. 15 circles containing the numbers 1 to 8 and the letters A to G distributed over a sheet of paper. Circles are connected by a pencil line in an alternate number-letter sequence. *Score:* number of seconds to completion. *Task Requirement:* sequential alternate identification of letters and numbers. *Stimulus:* spatially disarranged printed letters and numbers. *Response:* rapid coordination of complex sequential visual identification with a simple motor response.

D.   HALSTEAD'S NEUROPSYCHOLOGICAL TEST BATTERY (Halstead, 1947; Reitan, 1959, 1965).

21   CATEGORY TEST. 168 sets of visual choice stimuli, mostly geometric forms. On successive series of trials the abstraction of principles of numerosity, oddity, spatial position, and relative extent is required for correct responding. *Score:* total errors. *Task Requirement:* concept attainment by abstraction of common attributes of visual figures. *Stimulus:* visual figures. *Response:* choice among 4 response levers.

Tactual Performance Test (Measures 22-26)

This test requires placement of blocks in a Seguin-Goddard formboard while blindfolded. A six-block formboard is used for children 10 and 11 years old, and an eight-block board for children 12, 13, and 14 years old. The task is performed first with the preferred hand, next with the nonpreferred hand, and then with both hands. Finally, the subject draws a picture of the board, which he has never seen.

22   PREFERRED HAND. *Score:* number of seconds to correctly place all blocks. *Task Requirement:* place blocks in correct spaces on formboard. *Stimulus:* somesthetic perception of the formboard and forms. *Response:* complex somesthetic-motor coordination with preferred hand.

23   NONPREFERRED HAND. Same as Measure 22 except that nonpreferred hand is used.

24   BOTH HANDS. Same as Measures 22 and 23 except that both hands are used.

25   MEMORY. *Score:* number of forms correctly drawn from memory. *Task Requirement:* expression of somesthetic memory of drawing. *Stimulus:* instruction to draw formboard from memory. *Response:* drawing of formboard.

26   LOCATION. *Score:* number of forms in drawing correctly located with respect to position on formboard. Stimulus, task, and response same as above except that this aspect of the task requires memory of spatial location of forms.

Measure no.

27   RHYTHM TEST. 30 pairs of rhythmically patterned sounds. A judgment of "Same" or "Different" is required for each pair. *Score:* number correct. *Task Requirement:* discrimination of rhythmic similarity in pairs of auditory sound patterns. *Stimulus:* pairs of patterned sounds. *Response:* written *S* or *D* to denote judgment of same or different.

28   SPEECH PERCEPTION TEST. 60 tape-recorded monosyllabic nonsense words. Each word has a middle "ee" sound, and must be identified by means of a choice among 3 printed syllables. *Score:* number of errors. *Task Requirement:* match the spoken syllable with a printed syllable. *Stimulus:* spoken syllable and 3 printed syllables, one of which matches the spoken syllable. *Response:* underline printed syllable chosen.

29   TAPPING SPEED, PREFERRED HAND. The subject taps a mechanical counter as rapidly as possible with the index finger on 5 trials of 10 seconds each. *Score:* mean taps per 10 seconds. *Task Requirement:* achievement of maximum speed. *Stimulus:* instruction to tap as rapidly as possible. *Response:* rapid repetitive movement.

30   TAPPING SPEED, NONPREFERRED HAND. Same as Measure 29 except that the nonpreferred hand is used after completion of trials with the preferred hand.

31   TIME SENSE, VISUAL. 40 trials on which *S* stops the hand of a one-second sweep stop clock as close to zero as possible on its tenth rotation. *Score:* total error in seconds. *Task Requirement:* counting 10 rotations and then judging the proper time to stop the clock. *Stimulus:* visual observation of rotating hand on clock face. *Response:* maintenance of a motor set to hold down and release the response key at the proper time.

32   TIME SENSE, MEMORY. 20 trials interspersed among visual trials (Measure 31). The memory task is performed with no visual cues. *Task Requirement:* estimate of elapsed time. *Stimulus:* instruction to estimate time. *Response:* depression and release of reaction key.

E.   PEABODY PICTURE VOCABULARY TEST (Dunn, 1959).

33   PICTURE VOCABULARY, ORAL RAW SCORE. 150 sets of 4 line drawings, with which 150 words of increasing difficulty are to be associated. The words are those of Form B of the Peabody Vocabulary Test. *Score:* total correct picture-word associations. *Task Requirement:* selection of picture most appropriately related to the spoken word. *Stimulus:* 4 visual pictures, 1 spoken word. *Response:* simple pointing response.

34   PICTURE VOCABULARY, ORAL IQ. Transformation of oral raw score (Measure 33) to an IQ score on the basis of test norms (Dunn, 1959).

35   PICTURE VOCABULARY, WRITTEN RAW SCORE. 150 sets of 4 line drawings are associated with 150 printed words of increasing difficulty. The words are those of Form A of the Peabody Vocabulary Test. *Score:* total correct picture-word associations. *Task Requirement:* selection of picture most appropriately related to the printed word. *Stimulus:* 4 visual pictures, 1 word printed on a card. *Response:* simple pointing response.

Measure no.

F.   MODIFIED HALSTEAD-WEPMAN APHASIA SCREENING TEST (Halstead and Wepman, 1949; Heimburger and Reitan, 1961).

In its modified form this examination is designed to identify a number of language and nonlanguage disturbances, including disturbances of naming, spelling, reading, writing words, drawing pictures, calculation, articulation, and spatial orientation. Although the entire test was administered to all subjects, only the tests of construction apraxia were expressed as numbered measures.

Tests of Construction Apraxia (Measures 36-40).

36   COPY SQUARE. A two-inch printed square is copied as exactly as possible by a pencil drawing. *Score:* the rules for deriving a quantitative score were based on the rationale for scoring the Goodenough test (Goodenough, 1926). Points were assigned for motor coordination, length, angularity, and continuity to obtain a total accuracy score. *Task Requirement:* motor reproduction of visually perceived figure. *Stimulus:* printed two-inch square. *Response:* complex motor coordination to produce an exact drawing.

37   COPY CROSS. Same as Measure 36 except that a 1-3/4 inch Greek cross is copied.

38   COPY TRIANGLE. Same as Measure 36 except that an equilateral triangle with two-inch sides is copied.

39   COPY KEY. Same as Measure 36 except that a line drawing of a two-inch key is copied.

40   TOTAL DRAWING SCORE FOR HALSTEAD-WEPMAN TEST. Total score for measures 36, 37, 38, and 39.

G.   TESTS OF SENSORY-PERCEPTUAL DISTURBANCES (Reitan, 1965).

41   TACTILE SUPPRESSION RIGHT SIDE. The blindfolded *S* is simultaneously stimulated on the left and right side of the body by light touch. Various combinations of face and hand stimulation are presented. Incorrect localization or failure to perceive a stimulus is counted as an error. *Score:* number of errors for stimuli presented to the right side of the body. *Task Requirement:* correct identification and location of tactile stimuli. *Stimulus:* simultaneous bilateral touch. *Response:* simple pointing response or simple verbal report of the body areas stimulated.

42   TACTILE SUPPRESSION LEFT SIDE. This measure is derived for the left side of the body from the procedure described for Measure 41. *Score:* total errors for stimuli presented to the left side.

43   VISUAL SUPPRESSION, RIGHT VISUAL FIELD. Right and left visual fields are simultaneously stimulated by a simple confrontation procedure. Simultaneous stimulation trials are interspersed among unilateral stimulation trials. *Score:* number of trials on which a simultaneously presented stimulus to the right visual field is not perceived. *Task Requirement:* correct perception of bilateral simultaneous visual stimuli. *Stimulus:* bilateral simultaneous stimulation of the upper, middle, and lower portions of the visual fields. *Response:* simple verbal naming of the visual field or fields stimulated.

Measure no.

44   VISUAL SUPPRESSION, LEFT VISUAL FIELD. A measure of left visual suppression derived from the procedure described for Measure 43. *Score:* total number of trials on which *S* fails to perceive the stimuli presented to the left visual field during bilateral simultaneous stimulation.

45   FINGER AGNOSIA, RIGHT HAND. The blindfolded *S* is required to identify the finger of his right hand that has been touched, with each of the 5 fingers stimulated 4 times in unsystematic order. *Score:* number of trials on which a finger is incorrectly identified. *Task Requirement:* correct localization by a simple verbal designation of the finger stimulated. *Stimulus:* light tactile stimulation of the dorsal aspect of single fingers of the right hand. *Response:* simple verbal statement of the number or the name of the finger stimulated.

46   FINGER AGNOSIA, LEFT HAND. Same as Measure 45 except that the left hand is stimulated.

47   FINGER TIP NUMBER WRITING, RIGHT HAND. The examiner writes numbers on the finger tips of the blindfolded *S* with a pencil, and *S* is required to identify each number. *Score:* total incorrect identification in 20 trials (4 trials with each finger). *Task Requirement:* recognition of traced number. *Stimulus:* tactile — tracing of number on the fingertip. *Response:* spoken number.

48   FINGER TIP NUMBER WRITING, LEFT HAND. Same as Measure 47 except that left hand is stimulated.

49   TACTILE FORM RECOGNITION (ASTEREOGNOSIS), RIGHT HAND. The blindfolded *S* is required to identify coins placed in his hand. *Score:* total incorrect identifications in 6 trials. *Task Requirement:* recognition of coin by its tactile properties only. *Stimulus:* 2 trials each with a penny, a nickel, and dime. *Response:* spoken name of object.

50   TACTILE FORM RECOGNITION (ASTEREOGNOSIS), LEFT HAND. Same as Measure 49 except that the left hand is stimulated.

H.   LATERAL DOMINANCE EXAMINATION.

51   HAND PREFERENCE. *S* is required to demonstrate the hand used to throw a ball, hammer a nail, cut with a knife, turn a doorknob, use scissors, use an eraser, and write his name. *Score:* total number of acts performed with the preferred hand. *Task Requirement:* carry out the instruction by the use of one hand. *Stimulus:* verbal instruction, with object to be manipulated. *Response:* performance of a skilled act with one hand.

52   EYE PREFERENCE. *S* is given Miles' ABC Test of Ocular Dominance, in which he must choose one eye or the other to look through a conical aperture to identify a visual stimulus. *Score:* number of trials out of 10 on which *S* looks with the eye corresponding to the preferred hand. *Task Requirement:* identification of picture (*S* is presumed not to realize that only one eye is used for this test). *Stimulus:* visual line drawing on a card, viewed through aperture. *Response:* spoken identification of picture.

53   FOOT PREFERENCE. *S* is asked to demonstrate how he would kick a football and step on a bug. *Score:* number of trials out of 2 on which *S* uses the foot corresponding to the preferred hand. *Task Requirement:* use of a foot to carry out the verbal instruction. *Stimulus:* verbal instruction. *Response:* movement of a single foot.

Measure no.

54   STRENGTH OF GRIP, PREFERRED HAND. *S* is required to squeeze a hand dynamometer as hard as he can on 2 trials. *Score:* total pounds displacement of hand dynamometer dial on 2 trials. *Task Requirement:* exertion of maximum grip on hand dynamometer with preferred hand. *Stimulus:* spoken instruction. *Response:* gross flexor action of the preferred hand.

55   STRENGTH OF GRIP, NONPREFERRED HAND. Same as Measure 54 except that 2 trials with the nonpreferred hand are given.

56   WRITING SPEED, PREFERRED HAND. *S* is required to write his name with a pencil as rapidly as possible with his preferred hand. *Score:* time in seconds to write name. *Task Requirement:* rapid verbal-motor performance. *Stimulus:* verbal instruction. *Response:* rapid, skilled hand coordination.

57   WRITING SPEED, NONPREFERRED HAND. Same as Measure 56 except that the name is written with the nonpreferred hand.

II   *Modified Minnesota Test for Differential Diagnosis of Aphasia, Research Edition: Form 7 (Schuell, 1960)*

This test has 63 subtests divided into 6 categories. Certain subtests were modified to make them more appropriate for use with children. Other subtests were eliminated because the abilities tested therein were tested in other parts of the battery. In most cases the omitted tests are indicated below.

A.   AUDITORY DISTURBANCES.

—   (Hearing threshold for pure tones). Not done.

—   (Recognition of words). Identification of pictures in response to spoken words. See Measure 33.

58   RECOGNITION OF SYMBOLS. *S* is required to identify single letters of the alphabet by pointing. *Task Requirement:* identification of the printed letter which corresponds to the spoken letter. *Stimulus:* capital letters of the alphabet typewritten on a card in random sequence; spoken single letters. *Response:* spoken letter.

59   RETENTION SPAN: ITEMS NAMED SERIALLY. *S* is required to locate and point to 2 or 3 objects at a time in a picture. *Score:* number of presentations out of 6 on which 1 or more errors of identification are made, including omissions. *Task Requirement:* retention of the object's name, location of the objects in the picture, and pointing to the objects in the picture which correspond to the objects named. *Stimulus:* a large colored picture, with spoken names of 2 or 3 objects in the picture on each of the 6 trials. *Response:* simple pointing responses.

—   (Retention span: repetition of digits). See Wechsler Digit Span subtest, Measure 10.

60   RETENTION SPAN: REPETITION OF SENTENCES. *S* is required to repeat sentences ranging in length from three words to 18 words. *Score:* number of sentences incorrectly repeated out of 8 (part scores). *Task Requirement:* auditory reception, retention, and repetition of spoken sentence. *Stimulus:* spoken sentence. *Response:* spoken sentence.

Measure no.

61   FOLLOWING DIRECTIONS. *S* is required to carry out 10 spoken directions involving from 1 to 3 actions. *Score:* number of trials on which errors were made. *Task Requirement:* auditory reception and comprehension of spoken instructions, retention, and carrying out directions in proper sequence of actions. *Stimulus:* spoken directions, with visual array of simple objects. *Response:* a sequence of simple motor acts such as ringing a bell and opening a box.

62   PARAGRAPH COMPREHENSION. *S* is required to answer questions about a paragraph of 78 words which has been read to him. The paragraph tells a brief and simple story about a boy and a girl who visit an amusement park. *Score:* number of questions out of 7 incorrectly answered (part scores). *Task Requirement:* reception and comprehension of spoken paragraph; formulation of answers to questions on the basis of retention of the story content. *Stimulus:* spoken paragraph, followed by specific questions about the content of the paragraph (e.g., the name of the boy and girl). *Response:* spoken answers to questions.

B.   VISUAL AND READING DISTURBANCES.

63   MATCHING FORMS. *S* is required to select a form which matches a sample form from among a number of similar forms, with the sample form simultaneously present on half of the trials. *Score:* number of forms correctly identified out of 6. *Task Requirement:* identification from a number of alternatives of a form which matches the sample, with a different form used for each trial. *Stimulus:* line drawings of simple nonsense figures. *Response:* simple pointing response.

—   (Matching printed symbols). Not given.

64   MATCHING WORDS TO PICTURES. *S* is presented with a series of 16 line drawings. Each picture has 2 simple words printed underneath. *S* is required to point to the word which best matches the picture. *Score:* number of words incorrectly matched. *Task Requirement:* recognition of picture and silent reading of words. *Stimulus:* picture and printed words. *Response:* simple pointing response. (See also Picture Vocabulary, written raw score, Measure 10.)

65   PRINTED TO SPOKEN WORDS. For each of 25 pairs of printed words, *S* is required to point to the printed word which matches the spoken word. *Score:* number of words incorrectly identified on 16 trials. *Task Requirement:* simple reading response to determine the printed word which matches the spoken word. *Stimulus:* pairs of simple three- to seven-letter words printed on cards, with a spoken word that corresponds to 1 of the 2 printed words. *Response:* simple pointing response.

—   (Reading rate). Not given.

66   SENTENCE COMPREHENSION. *S* is required to read each of 7 printed questions and indicate the answer to each question. *Score:* number of incorrect answers out of seven. *Task Requirement:* comprehension of the meaning of a printed sentence. *Stimulus:* simple printed questions, with a printed *yes* and *no* following each question. *Response:* simple pointing response.

—   (Paragraph comprehension.) Not given.

Measure no.

—   (Oral reading: words.) See Measure 1, Reading.

67   ORAL READING: SENTENCES. *S* is required to read aloud 6 sentences composed of relatively simple words. *Score:* number of sentences incorrectly read (part scores). *Task Requirement:* simple oral reading response to sequences of printed words. *Stimulus:* printed sentence. *Response:* spoken sentence.

C.   SPEECH AND LANGUAGE DISTURBANCES.

—   (Gross movements of the Speech musculature). Not given.

—   (Rapid alternating movements). Not given.

68   ARTICULATION OF WORDS AND PHRASES. *S* is required to repeat 32 monosyllables, 7 polysyllabic words, and 10 three-word phrases. *Score:* number of words or phrases incorrectly articulated. *Task Requirement:* immediate vocal repetition of spoken word. *Stimulus:* spoken word or phrases. *Response:* complex articulatory movements to correctly form a spoken word or a phrase.

69   WORD FINDING: SENTENCE COMPLETION. *S* is required to supply the word which completes a simple spoken sentence. *Score:* number of inappropriate final words in 8 spoken sentences. *Task Requirement:* a guess as to a missing word in a sentence on the basis of common word sequences. *Stimulus:* incomplete spoken sentence. *Response:* spoken word.

70   WORD FINDING: SERIAL RESPONSES. *S* is asked to count to 20, name the days of the week, and name the months of the year in order. *Score:* number of numbers, days, or months omitted or named in incorrect order. *Task Requirement:* recall of related sequences of words. *Stimulus:* verbal instruction. *Response:* sequential naming.

71   WORD FINDING: RESPONSE TO QUESTIONS. *S* is required to give a spoken answer to each of eight simple spoken questions. *Score:* number of inappropriate responses. *Task Requirement:* comprehension of spoken question and formulation of an appropriate reply. *Stimulus:* spoken questions (e.g., "What do you tell time with?"). *Response:* simple spoken reply.

72   WORD FINDING: NAMING. *S* is required to supply appropriate names for each of 15 line drawings of familiar objects. *Score:* number of objects incorrectly named. *Task Requirement:* production of a spoken word appropriate to each picture. *Stimulus:* line drawing of familiar object. *Response:* spoken word.

73   WORD FINDING: RHYMES. *S* is required to emit as many words as he can think of that rhyme with each of 4 simple spoken words (go, tree, car, write). *Score:* total words correctly rhymed up to a limit of 5 rhymes per word. *Task Requirement:* formulation and emission of a series of rhyming words. *Stimulus:* spoken word, with instruction to emit rhyming words. *Response:* spoken words.

—   (Word finding: definitions) see Wechsler Vocabulary Subtest, Measure 13.

—   (Functional speech: giving information). Not given.

74   FUNCTIONAL SPEECH: EXPRESSING IDEAS. *S* is first asked to tell the examiner 3 things that he has done on the day that he is tested. Then he is asked to name all of the furniture that belongs in a living room. *Score:*

Measure no.

number of acts and objects named. *Task Requirement:* oral expression of simple recalled material. *Stimulus:* spoken instructions. *Response:* spoken words.

75　FUNCTIONAL SPEECH: PICTURE DESCRIPTION. *S* is shown a large color photograph of a small boy attempting to repair a small girl's tricycle and is asked to tell what is happening in the picture. *Score:* total number of words emitted during picture description. *Task Requirement:* formulation and verbalization of a spoken description of the objects and events in the picture. *Stimulus:* visual picture with spoken instruction to describe picture. *Response:* spoken narrative.

76　SIMPLE FORMULATION: SENTENCES. For each of a series of 6 words, *S* is given a single word and told to formulate a sentence which contains this word. *Score:* number of sentences with incorrect usage of the word (part scores). *Task Requirement:* formulation of an appropriate sequence of words which includes the given word. *Stimulus:* spoken word with instruction to use it in a sentence. *Response:* spoken sentence.

—　(Complex formulation: similarities) see Wechsler Similarities Subtest, Measure 12.

77　COMPLEX FORMULATION: RETELLING PARAGRAPH. A sixty-eight-word paragraph about quicksand is read aloud to *S*. *S* is asked to listen for the most important ideas and then tell the examiner as much as he can remember about the paragraph. *Score:* the number of correct statements given, out of 6 major statements about quicksand in the paragraph (part scores). *Task Requirement:* comprehension, short-term recall and oral expression of explicit information. *Stimulus:* spoken paragraph. *Response:* spoken statements.

D.　VISUAL MOTOR AND WRITING DISTURBANCES.

78　COPYING COMPLEX FIGURE. *S* is required to make a pencil copy of a nonrepresentational figure. *Score:* rules similar to those used for Measures 36-39, with individual points for specific features of the drawing combined into a total accuracy score. *Task Requirement:* reproduction of a nonrepresentational figure. *Stimulus:* line drawing of a complex figure 2-1/2″ in height printed on a card. *Response:* complex motor coordination to produce exact pencil movement.

79　DRAWING A HOUSE. *S* is told to make a pencil drawing of a house on a blank sheet of 8-1/2″ x 11″ paper. *Score:* a total accuracy score derived from points given for completeness, general accuracy, and motor coordination, as in the Draw-a-Person test (Goodenough, 1926). *Task Requirement:* visual recall of the details of a house, with accurate drawing of these details. *Stimulus:* spoken instruction to draw a house. *Response:* complex motor coordination to produce an accurate drawing from memory.

80　DRAWING A MAN. *S* is told to make a pencil drawing of a man on an 8-1/2″ x 11″ piece of paper. *Score:* according to rules formulated by Goodenough (1926). *Task Requirement:* recall and accurate reproduction of a human figure. *Stimulus:* instruction to draw a man. *Response:* complex motor coordination to produce an accurate drawing from memory.

81　REPRODUCING WHEEL. *S* is briefly shown a line drawing of a wheel, and then is asked to draw it from memory. *Score:* as in Measure 78. *Task*

Measure no.

Requirement: short-term visual recall of drawing, and accurate reproduction on the basis of recall. Stimulus: drawing of a wagon wheel 2-1/4" in diameter with spokes, rim, and hub, with the instruction to recall the drawing. Response: complex motor coordination in reproducing drawing.

82   TOTAL DRAWING SCORE FOR SCHUELL TEST. Sum of drawing scores obtained on Measures 78 through 81.

83   REPRODUCING LETTERS. S is shown a series of 12 printed letters and 3 simple printed words and is asked to reproduce each from memory. Score: total errors. Task Requirement: recall and reproduction of visual letter and word stimuli. Stimulus: printed letter or word, with each letter exposed for 2 seconds and each word for 4 seconds, and instruction to reproduce from memory. Response: writing word or letter.

—   (Object assembly: head) see Measure 17.

84   NUMERALS TO TWENTY. S is asked to write the numbers 1 to 20 on a piece of paper. Score: total errors. Task Requirement: recall and reproduction of a simple sequence of numbers. Stimulus: instruction to write a sequence of numbers. Response: simple sequential writing response.

85   LETTERS TO DICTATION. S is asked to write the letters of the alphabet to dictation, as presented in unsystematic order. Score: total errors. Task Requirement: written reproduction of a spoken letter. Stimulus: spoken letters. Response: simple writing response.

86   WORDS, VISUAL STIMULUS. S is shown a series of simple line drawings and is asked to write the name of the object in each picture. Score: number of words incorrectly spelled. Task Requirement: formulation and writing of a name associated with a picture. Stimulus: line drawing of a simple object with instruction to write the name of the word which corresponds to the object. Response: word writing.

—   (Words auditory stimulus) see Measure 2.

—   (Written spelling) see Measure 2.

87   ORAL SPELLING. 24 words of increasing difficulty taken from the Wide Range Achievement Test are spoken to S, who is required to spell each word aloud until he has missed 3 consecutive words. Score: total words correctly spelled. Task Requirement: oral emission of the letters in a spoken word. Stimulus: spoken word, along with an example of the word as used in a sentence. Response: spoken letter sequence.

88   SENTENCES TO DICTATION. 8 sentences ranging in length from 2 to 16 words are read aloud to S. S is required to write each sentence as it is read. Score: total sentences incorrectly written (part scores). Task Requirement: short-term recall and written reproduction of spoken sentence. Stimulus: spoken sentence. Response: complex sequential writing behavior.

89   SPONTANEOUS SENTENCES. S is asked to write sentences in which each of 6 simple words are correctly used. Score: total number of sentences with incorrect usage or misspelling (part score). Task Requirement: formulation and writing of a sentence which contains the given word. Stimulus: written word. Response: complex sequential writing response.

90   SPONTANEOUS PARAGRAPH. S is once again shown the picture used for Measure 75 and is asked to write a description of what is happening in the picture. Score: total words correctly spelled. Task Requirement:

Measure no.

formulation and writing of a picture description. *Stimulus:* picture, with verbal instruction. *Response:* complex sequential writing response.

III *Other Psychological Tests*

A. SPEED OF VISUAL PERCEPTION

These tests were developed especially for the present investigation. They are intended to assess speed and accuracy of visual discrimination for various kinds of verbal and nonverbal visual stimuli presented singly and in combination. In general, the visual stimulus becomes more verbal and more complex with each succeeding test. The first and the last subtests involve the same task in order to permit assessment of practice effect.

91 SINGLE NUMBER. *S* is required to underline the number 4 each time it appears on a printed page containing a random sequence of 360 single numbers. An example of the number to be identified is printed at the top of the page. A short practice test is given. *Score:* total numbers correctly underlined minus total incorrectly underlined in 30 seconds. *Task Requirement:* locating and underlining a particular number interspersed among other numbers. *Stimulus:* random sequences of printed numbers. *Response:* simple underlining response to identify single numbers.

92 SINGLE GEOMETRIC FORMS. *S* is required to underline a Greek cross with a pencil each time it appears in random sequence among a series of 235 geometric forms, including squares, stars, circles, triangles, etc. The forms are about 1/4″ in height. *Score:* total crosses underlined minus total errors in 30 seconds. *Task Requirements:* as in Measure 91, but for identification of a geometric form.

93 SINGLE NONSENSE LETTER. A single nonsense letter is interspersed among 10 structurally similar nonsense letters in a random sequence of 126 letters. *Score:* total correct minus incorrect underlined letters. *Task Requirement:* as in Measure 91, but for identification of a nonsense letter.

94 GESTALT FIGURE. The figure to be identified is a diamond about 1-1/2″ in height containing a square which in turn contains a diamond. This figure is interspersed among similar figures in a random sequence of 168 figures. *Score:* total correct minus incorrect underlined figures in 60 seconds. *Task Requirement:* as in Measure 91, but for identification of a complex figure.

95 SINGLE LETTER. The letter "s" is interspersed among 360 randomized letters. *Score:* number underlined minus number of errors in 30 seconds. *Task Requirement:* as in Measure 91, but for a single letter.

96 SINGLE LETTER IN SYLLABLE CONTEXT. 162 four-letter nonsense syllables are presented, 47 of which contain the letter "e." *S* is required to underline each syllable containing "e." *Score:* total correct minus incorrect in 45 seconds. *Task Requirement:* as in Measure 91, but for a letter in syllable context.

97 TWO LETTERS. This task is same as Measure 95, except that *S* is required to underline 2 letters ("b" and "m") instead of a single letter in the context of other single letters. The time limit is 45 seconds.

Measure no.

98   SEQUENCE OF GEOMETRIC FORMS. 4 geometric forms (triangle, Greek cross, circle, crescent) are presented in various orders for a total of 65 "syllables." *S* is required to underline only the groups with the order triangle, cross, crescent, and circle. *Score:* total groups correctly underlined minus errors in 60 seconds. *Task Requirement:* same as Measure 91, but for groups of geometric figures.

99   FOUR LETTER NONSENSE SYLLABLE, UNPRONOUNCEABLE. *S* is required to underline a four-letter nonsense syllable (fsbm) interspersed among 146 four-letter nonsense syllables. All syllables are made up of consonants, which renders them unpronounceable. *Score:* total correct minus incorrect in 60 seconds. *Task Requirement:* same as Measure 91, but for nonsense syllables.

100   FOUR LETTER NONSENSE SYLLABLE, PRONOUNCEABLE. This task is the same as Measure 99 except that it involves the identification of a pronounceable nonsense syllable (narp) instead of an unpronounceable nonsense syllable. This syllable is interspersed among other nonsense syllables made up of the letters n, a, r, p. The time limit is 60 seconds.

101   FOUR LETTER WORD. The word "spot" is interspersed among 146 four-letter syllables made up of the letters s, p, o, t. *Score:* total correct minus incorrect in 60 seconds. *Task Requirement:* same as Measure 91, but for a four-letter word.

102   UNSPACED FOUR LETTER WORD. The word "spot" is interspersed among the letters s, p, o, t, in various orders, with no syllabic spacing. *Score:* total correct minus incorrect. *Task Requirement:* same as Measure 91, but for an unspaced word.

103   SINGLE NUMBER. This task is exactly the same as that involved in Measure 91 except that the number to be underlined is 5 instead of 4.

B.   TESTS OF RELEVANT ABILITIES NOT ASSESSED ELSEWHERE.

104   SPATIAL ORIENTATION. *S* is required to identify his own body parts and those of the examiner in various combinations in relation to right-left orientation. A total of 14 items are given, including 5 items on which *S* identifies a lateralized part of his body, 2 trials on which *S* indicates a lateralized part of the examiner's body, 2 trials on which *S* indicates lateralization on a picture of wearing apparel, 2 trials on which *S* is asked to use a lateralized body part, and 2 trials on which *S* imitates lateralized movements by the examiner. *Score:* total errors. *Task Requirement:* correct designation of body orientation. *Stimulus:* verbal instruction or demonstration. *Response:* simple pointing response, or controlled movement, in some cases with a designated arm.

105   THE THURSTONE REVERSALS TEST. *S* is shown 88 pairs of line drawings. About half of the pairs contain identical drawings, while the other half consist of mirror-image figures. *S* is required to designate which pairs are the same and which pairs are different. *Score:* total errors. *Task Requirement:* determination of the right-left orientation of drawings in relation to each other. *Stimulus:* pairs of visual figures. *Response:* simple verbal statement of same or different.

Measure no.

106   WORD ASSOCIATION TEST. 18 words are presented by a conventional free association procedure. The grammatical categories of the words included 3 words from each of the following classes: count nouns, mass nouns, adjectives, transitive verbs, intransitive verbs and adverbs. *S*'s response is counted as correct if the grammatical category of the response word was the same as that of the stimulus word. *Score:* percentage of correct responses. *Task Requirement:* emission of habitual verbal association, as indicative of the developmental stage of language habits. *Stimulus:* spoken word, with instruction to respond with the first word that comes to mind. *Response:* spoken word.

107   COLOR FORM TEST. *S* is presented with groups of 3 visual stimuli which could differ from each other in color, shape, and size and is required to point to the figure that he judges to be most different among the 3 forms. There is no "correct" choice, since at least 2 of the 3 figures differed from the other figures by at least 2 attributes. *Score:* percent of trials out of 20 of which *S*'s choice is based upon the attribute of shape. *Task Requirement:* an "oddity" problem, requiring a judgment of difference. *Stimulus:* group of 3 visual figures systematically differing in color, size, and shape. *Response:* simple pointing response.

108   VISUAL MEMORY FOR FIGURES: SPATIAL. *S* is shown a card containing a sequence of different geometric shapes. Upon removal of the card he is asked to indicate on a multiple choice card the shapes which were shown, preserving their original left-to-right order. Sequences of from 2 to 6 shapes are shown in this manner. A maximum of 15 trials are given. *Score:* total errors. *Task Requirement:* short-term recall of nonverbal sequences. *Stimulus:* sequence of visual figures. *Response:* series of simple pointing responses.

109   VISUAL MEMORY FOR FIGURES: TEMPORAL. This test is the same as Measure 108, except that the visual figures are shown one at a time in temporal sequence instead of in a spatial sequence. Short-term recall of nonverbal temporal sequences is required.

Forms Completed during Interview with Parent

1. BIRTH AND DEVELOPMENTAL HISTORY

Subject's Name _____

Address _____

Telephone _____ Place of Birth _____

I. *Pregnancy and Delivery*

    A. Pregnancy complications:
        1. Diseases _____
        2. Bleeding and other _____
    B. Delivery:
        1. Length of term _____
        2. Duration of labor _____
        3. Type of delivery _____

        4. O_2 administration or time in incubator (duration) _____
        5. Birth length _____ 6. Birth weight _____
        7. General condition at birth _____
        8. Comparison of pregnancy and delivery with that of other siblings ___
        _____

II. *Development*

    A. Neonatal feeding problems _____
    B. Age of (comparison with siblings):
        1. Holding up head _____
        2. Sitting up _____
        3. Crawling _____
        4. Talking:
           a. words _____
           b. sentences _____
        5. Standing with help _____;
           Standing alone _____
        6. Walking _____
    C. Toilet training _____
        _____age begun _____ age ended _____
    D. Other languages used in the home _____

III. *Illness and Accidents*

    A. Illnesses (severity of each illness) _____

    B. Accidents (fractures, stitches, etc.) _____

    C. High fever (specify temperature) _____

III. *Illness and Accidents* (contd.)

    D. Convulsions (cause) _____
                           No. _____ Age _____
    E. Unconsciousness (duration) _____
    F. Head injuries _____
    G. Operations (No. and type) _____
    H. Coordination problems (riding bicycle) _____
    I. Other difficulties _____

IV. *Education*

    A. Age started to school _____
    B. Grades repeated (specify) _____
    C. Present grades being made by subject:
        1. Reading _____
        2. Mathematics _____
        3. Spelling _____
        4. Social Studies _____
        5. Other _____
    D. School History (names and dates of each school attended): _____
    _____

V. *Siblings*

    A. Names and ages:
        1. _____ _____
        2. _____ _____
        3. _____ _____
        4. _____ _____
    B. Pregnancy complications _____
    C. Developmental complications (including seizures) _____
    _____
    D. General health _____

VI. *Handedness*

    A. Child _____
    B. Father _____
    C. Mother _____
    D. Siblings 1. _____ 2. _____ 3. _____ 4. _____

VII. *Present situation*

    1. Vision _____
    2. Hearing _____
    3. Speech _____
    4. Daily routine: Eating _____
           Sleeping _____
           Self Care _____
    5. Activities (sports, music, books, TV) _____
    _____
    6. Tasks (household; jobs) _____
    _____
    7. Relationship with peer group _____
    8. Home situation _____
    9. Effect of reading difficulty upon social relationships in school _____
    _____

VIII. *Informant* (Reliability) _____

_____

2. FAMILY HISTORY OF READING PROBLEMS

Subject's Name _____

        Age _____ Grade _____

I. *Parents*

    1. Mother:

        (a) Do you have any reading difficulty? Yes _____ No _____

        (b) Do you read a daily newspaper? Yes _____ No _____
            If so, which newspaper? _____

        (c) Do you read any magazines? Yes _____ No _____
            If so, what magazines do you read? _____

        (d) Do you read books? Yes _____ No _____
            If so, what books have you read recently? _____

        (e) What is the highest grade you completed in school? _____

    2. Father:

        (a) Do you have any reading difficulty? Yes_____ No _____

        (b) Do you read a daily newspaper? Yes _____ No _____
            If so, which newspaper? _____

        (c) Do you read any magazines? Yes _____ No _____
            If so, what magazines do you read? _____

        (d) Do you read books? Yes _____ No _____
            If so, what books have you read recently? _____

        (e) What is the highest grade you completed in school? _____

II. *Siblings*

    (a) Do you have any other children? Yes _____ No _____

    (b) Have any of them had difficulty in learning how to read? Yes__ No__
        Any present reading problems? Yes _____ No _____

    (c) Have any of your children ever been held back a year in school?
                Yes _____ No _____

    (d) What is the highest grade that each of your children have completed in
        school? _____; _____; _____; _____; _____.

III. *Mother's siblings*

    (a) Have any of your brothers or sisters had any reading difficulty?
                Yes _____ No _____

    (b) What was the highest grade completed in school by each of them?
        _____; _____; _____; _____; _____.

IV. *Father's siblings*

    (a) Have any of your brothers or sisters had any reading difficulty?
                Yes _____ No _____

    (b) What was the highest grade in school completed by each of them?
        _____; _____; _____; _____; _____.

V. *Grandparents*

   (1) Mother's parents:
     (a) Has either your mother or your father had any reading difficulty?
               Yes _____ No _____
       If so, which one? _____
     (b) What grade did your mother complete? _____ Father? _____
   (2) Father's parents:
     (a) Has either your mother or your father had any reading difficulty?
               Yes _____ No _____
       If so, which one? _____
     (b) What grade did you mother complete? _____ Father? _____

VI. *Other Relatives*

   (a) Mother's relatives: Have any other relatives in your family had reading difficulties? Yes _____ No _____
     If so, which ones? _____
     Grade level _____
   (b) Father's relatives: Have any other relatives in your family had reading difficulties? Yes _____ No _____
     If so, which ones? _____
     Grade level _____

VII. *Subject*

   (a) Did subject have any difficulty learning to read? _____
   (b) Was subject ever held back in school because of this difficulty? _____
     _____
   (c) Does the subject do much reading outside of school work? _____
     (1) A daily newspaper? _____
     (2) Any magazines? _____
     (3) Any books? _____
     (4) Comic books? _____

VIII. *Comments*

_____
_____
_____

Results of Test-by-Test Comparisons
of Retarded Readers and Normal Readers
by Analysis of Covariance

Column 1. Measure The number and order of measures corresponds to their listing in Appendix A.
Column 2. Group N = 39 Male Normal Readers, R = 39 Retarded Readers.
Column 3. Mean Average score in the units given in Appendix A.
Column 4. SD Standard deviation.
Column 5. Dist. Characteristics of distribution, as follows:
  OK. Adequate dispersion of scores.
  1. Many perfect or near-perfect scores.
  2. Almost all scores perfect.
  3. Small number of scoring categories.
Column 6. F' Statistical ratio obtained by analysis of covariance.
Column 7. Sign. level Level of statistical significance of F' ratio.
Column 8. Direct. Direction of superiority. N: Normal Readers significantly superior; R: Retarded Readers significantly superior.

Measure	Group	Mean	SD	Dist.	F'	Sign. Level	Direct.
Wide Range Achievement Test							
1. Reading (grade level)	N	8.0	1.5	OK	324.8	.001	N
	R	3.5	1.3	OK			
2. Spelling (grade level)	N	7.3	1.6	OK	260.7	.001	N
	R	3.2	1.2	OK			
Wechsler-Bellevue Intelligence Scale, Form I							
3. Full Scale IQ	N	107.8	8.8	OK	33.6	.001	N
	R	96.2	9.5	OK			
4. Verbal IQ	N	107.2	8.1	OK	113.3	.001	N
	R	86.5	9.0	OK			
5. Performance IQ	N	106.8	11.4	OK	0.0	n.s.	–
	R	107.0	10.4	OK			
6. Verbal Weighted Score	N	45.2	8.1	OK	107.1	.001	N
	R	31.1	7.0	OK			
7. Performance Weighted Score	N	47.0	7.6	OK	0.0	n.s.	–
	R	47.3	7.4	OK			
8. Information (weighted score)	N	9.1	1.9	OK	99.0	.001	N
	R	5.6	1.8	OK			
9. Comprehension (weighted score)	N	9.9	2.3	OK	10.9	.01	N
	R	8.3	2.5	OK			
10. Digit Span (weighted score)	N	7.4	2.6	OK	10.3	.01	N
	R	5.7	2.6	OK			
11. Arithmetic (weighted score)	N	8.5	3.2	OK	56.7	.001	N
	R	3.8	2.9	OK			

Measure	Group	Mean	SD	Dist.	F'	Sign. Level	Direct.
Wechsler-Bellevue Intelligence Scale, Form I (cont.)							
12. Similarities	N	10.2	1.5	OK	51.8	.001	N
(weighted score)	R	7.6	1.7	OK			
13. Vocabulary	N	8.5	1.7	OK	45.8	.001	N
(weighted score)	R	6.6	1.4	OK			
14. Picture Arrangement	N	9.3	3.2	OK	0.2	n.s.	–
(weighted score)	R	9.0	3.4	OK			
15. Picture Completion	N	9.4	2.6	OK	2.5	n.s.	–
(weighted score)	R	10.3	2.5	OK			
16. Block Design	N	10.0	2.2	OK	1.1	n.s.	–
(weighted score)	R	9.5	2.3	OK			
17. Object Assembly	N	9.7	2.4	OK	9.8	.01	R
(weighted score)	R	11.3	1.9	OK			
18. Digit Symbol	N	8.5	1.8	OK	13.9	.001	N
(weighted score)	R	7.2	2.0	OK			
Trail Making Test							
19. Part A. Numbers	N	14.7	4.1	OK	20.9	.001	N
(total time in sec.)	R	21.2	8.3	OK			
20. Part B. Letters & Num-	N	32.3	12.4	OK	13.9	.001	N
bers (total time in sec.)	R	47.8	24.4	OK			
Halstead's Neuropsychological Test Battery							
21. Category Test	N	39.2	16.3	OK	9.7	.01	N
(total errors)	R	50.3	15.7	OK			
Tactual Performance Test (Measures 22-26)							
22. Preferred Hand	N	6.3	2.2	OK	15.9	.001	R
(time in min.)	R	4.5	1.8	OK			
23. Nonpreferred Hand	N	3.5	2.0	OK	2.1	n.s.	–
(time in min.)	R	3.0	1.7	OK			
24. Both Hands	N	1.9	1.1	OK	4.2	.05	R
(time in min.)	R	1.5	0.6	OK			
25. Memory	N	5.5	1.6	OK	0.2	n.s.	–
(correct shapes)	R	5.4	1.4	OK			
26. Location	N	3.8	1.8	OK	1.0	n.s.	–
(correct locations)	R	3.5	1.6	OK			
27. Rhythm Test	N	26.3	2.3	1	25.2	.001	N
(total correct)	R	22.4	4.6	OK			
28. Speech Perception	N	5.3	2.8	1	55.6	.001	N
(total errors)	R	16.9	10.1	OK			
29. Tapping, preferred hand	N	40.0	5.9	OK	1.2	n.s.	–
(taps/10 sec.)	R	38.9	5.7	OK			
30. Tapping, nonpreferred	N	36.8	4.6	OK	3.9	n.s.	–
hand (taps/10 sec.)	R	35.0	5.2	OK			
31. Time Sense Visual	N	75.7	41.9	OK	6.5	.05	N
(total error in sec.)	R	118.0	104.2	OK			
32. Time Sense Memory	N	335.5	242.5	OK	3.5	n.s.	–
(total error in sec.)	R	242.3	141.8	OK			
Peabody Picture Vocabulary Test							
33. Oral Vocabulary	N	100.9	13.1	OK	17.9	.001	N
(total correct)	R	92.5	10.0	OK			
34. Oral Vocabulary	N	112.4	12.8	OK	18.1	.001	N
(IQ score)	R	101.6	9.2	OK			
35. Written Vocabulary	N	97.3	11.6	OK	118.8	.001	N
(total correct)	R	57.5	25.3	OK			

Measure	Group	Mean	SD	Dist.	F'	Sign. Level	Direct.
from *Modified Halstead-Wepman Aphasia Screening Test*							
36. Copy Square	N	9.5	1.3	OK	0.2	n.s.	–
(accuracy score)	R	9.6	1.1	OK			
37. Copy Cross	N	10.4	2.0	OK	4.2	.05	N
(accuracy score)	R	9.4	2.1	OK			
38. Copy Triangle	N	8.8	0.7	OK	0.2	n.s.	–
(accuracy score)	R	8.9	1.1	OK			
39. Copy Key	N	16.5	2.8	OK	0.1	n.s.	–
(accuracy score)	R	16.7	3.0	OK			
40. Total Drawing Score	N	45.2	4.6	OK	0.2	n.s.	–
(total measures 36-39)	R	44.7	4.8	OK			
Additional Tests for Sensory and Perceptual Disturbances							
41. Tactile Suppression,	N	0.3	0.6	2	0.7	n.s.	–
right (errors)	R	0.4	0.8	2			
42. Tactile Suppression,	N	0.3	0.5	2	0.1	n.s.	–
left (errors)	R	0.2	0.5	2			
43. Visual Suppression,	N	0.2	0.6	2	0.0	n.s.	–
right (errors)	R	0.2	0.6	2			
44. Visual Suppression,	N	0.2	0.5	2	0.0	n.s.	–
left (errors)	R	0.2	0.5	2			
45. Finger Agnosia, right	N	1.2	1.5	2	3.9	n.s.	–
(errors)	R	2.0	2.2	2			
46. Finger Agnosia, left	N	1.2	1.7	2	6.5	.05	N
(errors)	R	2.4	2.4	2			
47. Finger Tip Writing,	N	3.8	3.8	1	0.6	n.s.	–
right (errors)	R	4.4	3.3	1			
48. Finger Tip Writing,	N	3.8	3.8	1	1.0	n.s.	–
left (errors)	R	3.1	3.2	1			
49. Astereognosis, right	N	2.1	1.4	OK	6.4	.05	R
(errors)	R	1.4	1.1	OK			
50. Astereognosis, left	N	2.4	1.3	OK	4.4	.05	R
(errors)	R	1.7	1.2	OK			
Lateral Dominance Tests							
51. Hand Preference	N	6.9	0.5	2	0.0	n.s.	–
(total preferred)	R	6.9	0.5	2			
52. Eye Preference	N	7.2	4.1	2,3	0.0	n.s.	–
(total preferred)	R	7.1	4.1	2,3			
53. Foot Preference	N	1.7	0.6	2,3	0.6	n.s.	–
(total preferred)	R	1.8	0.5	2,3			
54. Grip Strength,	N	28.2	9.4	OK	7.0	.01	N
preferred (lbs.)	R	24.2	9.5	OK			
55. Grip Strength,	N	25.6	8.6	OK	4.5	.05	N
nonpreferred (lbs.)	R	22.5	9.2	OK			
56. Writing Speed,	N	10.5	2.7	OK	1.5	n.s.	–
preferred (sec.)	R	11.7	5.7	OK			
57. Writing Speed,	N	26.4	7.0	OK	2.4	n.s.	–
nonpreferred (sec.)	R	29.7	11.5	OK			
from *Modified Minnesota Test for Differential Diagnosis of Aphasia*							
A. *Auditory Disturbances*							
58. Symbol Recognition	N	0.0	0.2	2	4.8	.05	N
(errors)	R	0.5	1.3	2			
59. Retention of Serial Items	N	0.08		2	no		
(errors)	R	0.05		2	test		

	Measure	Group	Mean	SD	Dist.	F'	Sign. Level	Direct.
	A. *Auditory Disturbances* (cont.)							
60.	Sentence Repetition	N	1.3	0.7	OK	12.7	.001	N
	(errors)	R	1.8	0.7	OK			
61.	Following Directions	N	0.1		2	no		
	(errors)	R	0.1		2	test		
62.	Paragraph Comprehen-	N	0.7	0.7	1	5.6	.05	N
	sion (errors)	R	1.2	1.0	1			
	B. *Visual and Reading Disturbances*							
63.	Matching Forms	N	0.7	0.9	2	0.8	n.s.	-
	(errors)	R	0.5	0.8	2			
64.	Matching Words &	N	0.0	0.2	2	15.81	.001	N
	Pictures (errors)	R	0.8	1.2	2			
65.	Printed to Spoken Words	N	0.0	0.0	2	5.0	.05	N
	(errors)	R	0.4	1.2	2			
66.	Sentence Comprehension	N	0.1	0.3	2	16.4	.001	N
	(errors)	R	0.9	1.4	2			
67.	Oral Reading Sentences	N	0.2	0.8	2	32.7	.001	N
	(errors)	R	2.0	2.0	1			
	C. *Speech and Language Disturbances*							
68.	Articulation	N	0.8	0.8	1	18.0	.001	N
	(errors)	R	2.4	2.4	1			
69.	Sentence Completion	N	0.6	0.7	2	0.8	n.s.	-
	(errors)	R	0.7	0.8	1			
70.	Serial Responses	N	0.3	0.7	2	46.2	.001	N
	(errors)	R	3.6	3.2	1			
71.	Response to Questions	N	0.0		2	no		
	(errors)	R	0.0		2	test		
72.	Naming	N	0.0		2	no		
	(errors)	R	0.1		2	test		
73.	Rhymes	N	19.0	1.6	2	107.3	.001	N
	(correct in 20)	R	10.5	4.9	OK			
74.	Expressing Ideas	N	10.3	2.4	OK	3.4	n.s.	-
	(total ideas)	R	9.5	1.5	OK			
75.	Picture Description	N	85.5	51.7	OK	2	n.s.	-
	(total words)	R	80.3	58.2	OK			
76.	Sentence Formulation	N	0.3	0.4	1	6.5	.005	-
	(errors)	R	0.6	0.6	1			
77.	Retelling Paragraph	N	4.5	0.8	OK	12.9	.001	N
	(correct statements)	R	3.9	0.8	OK			
	D. *Visual Motor and Writing Disturbances*							
78.	Copy Complex Figure	N	11.9	1.9	OK	16.1	.001	N
	(accuracy score)	R	10.2	2.0	OK			
79.	Draw House	N	17.4	3.1	OK	1.2	n.s.	-
	(accuracy score)	R	16.6	3.1	OK			
80.	Draw a Man	N	31.9	7.2	OK	20.6	.001	N
	(accuracy score)	R	24.9	6.6	OK			
81.	Reproduce Wheel	N	13.5	2.7	OK	3.6	n.s.	-
	(accuracy score)	R	12.4	2.6	OK			
82.	Total Schuell Drawings	N	74.6	10.3	OK	21.3	.001	N
	(accuracy)	R	64.1	10.3	OK			

Measure	Group	Mean	SD	Dist.	F'	Sign. Level	Direct.
D. Visual Motor and Writing Disturbances (cont.)							
83. Reproduce Letters (errors)	N	0.1		2	no		
	R	0.8		2	test		
84. Numerals to 20 (errors)	N	0.0		2	no		
	R	0.2		2	test		
85. Letters to Dictation (errors)	N	0.0	0.0	2	5.5	.05	N
	R	0.6	1.7	2			
86. Words, Visual Stimulus (errors)	N	0.1	0.3	2	86.2	.001	N
	R	3.5	2.4	OK			
87. Oral Spelling (correct)	N	16.9	4.3	OK	243.3	.001	N
	R	5.8	3.2	OK			
88. Sentences to Dictation (errors)	N	0.7	0.7	2	198.9	.001	N
	R	4.8	1.9	OK			
89. Spontaneous Sentences (errors)	N	0.2	0.4	2	51.0	.001	N
	R	1.7	1.3	OK			
90. Spontaneous Paragraph (total correct words)	N	75.7	24.6	OK	68.4	.001	N
	R	32.5	22.6	OK			
Speed of Visual Perception							
91. Single Numbers (correct)	N	31.7	6.0	OK	10.0	.01	N
	R	27.3	7.5	OK			
92. Single Geometric Forms (correct)	N	34.8	5.5	OK	19.4	.001	N
	R	28.6	7.3	OK			
93. Single Nonsense Letters (correct)	N	20.2	3.3	OK	24.0	.00	N
	R	16.1	4.9	OK			
94. Gestalt Figures (correct)	N	9.9	4.7	OK	8.2	.01	N
	R	7.3	3.9	OK			
95. Single Letters (correct)	N	23.8	3.8	OK	12.6	.001	N
	R	20.8	5.1	OK			
96. Letter in Syllable (correct)	N	19.4	4.2	OK	16.0	.001	N
	R	16.3	4.5	OK			
97. Two Single Letters (correct)	N	16.7	2.7	OK	3.8	n.s.	-
	R	15.5	4.1	OK			
98. Sequence of Geometric Forms (correct)	N	8.9	2.2	OK	8.8	.01	N
	R	7.6	2.1	OK			
99. Unpronounceable Syllables (correct)	N	9.9	3.2	OK	17.0	.001	N
	R	7.4	2.6	OK			
100. Pronounceable Syllables (correct)	N	16.0	3.3	OK	74.0	.001	N
	R	9.4	3.9	OK			
101. Four Letter Word (correct)	N	16.7	2.9	OK	49.2	.001	N
	R	11.1	4.9	OK			
102. Unspaced Four Letter Word (correct)	N	9.9	2.0	OK	43.4	.001	N
	R	6.9	2.6	OK			
103. Single Number (correct)	N	26.9	4.9	OK	8.7	.01	N
	R	23.7	6.2	OK			
Other Tests							
104. Spatial Orientation (errors)	N	1.9	2.0	1	4.4	.05	N
	R	2.8	1.7	OK			
105. Reversals (errors)	N	5.1	4.9	1	25.9	.001	N
	R	12.2	7.4	OK			
106. Word Association (percent correct)	N	58.2	20.3	OK	0.1	n.s.	-
	R	60.0	20.5	OK			
107. Color Form (percent form)	N	73.6	23.7	OK	0.2	n.s.	-
	R	76.2	24.4	OK			

Measure	Group	Mean	SD	Dist.	F′	Sign. Level	Direct.
D. *Visual Motor and Writing Disturbances* (cont.)							
108. Visual Spatial Memory (errors)	N	10.3	5.0	OK	20.3	.001	N
	R	16.0	6.7	OK			
109. Visual Temporal Memory (errors)	N	8.8	5.2	OK	20.9	.001	N
	R	15.0	7.0	OK			

Instructions Used by the Two Judges for
Rating the Probability of Cerebral Dysfunction
in Individual Subjects

No brain damage: We will accept variations in levels of ability within the normal range and mild indications that might be suspicious of brain dysfunction. We will not accept pronounced intraindividual variations on lateralized sensory or motor performance. The variations from normality that will be acceptable are ones that occur on measures of ability level rather than on measures of lateralized performances.

Brain damage: An indication of brain damage may be supported by consistently poor levels of test results, but in most instances should be substantiated by evidence of lateralized sensory and motor dysfunction. In most instances the actual level of performance will not be the sole criterion, but should be supported by evidence of dysfunction in simple sensory and motor functions on the 2 sides of the body regardless of whether or not a marked disparity on the 2 sides of the body occurs.

Minimal: This classification will include subjects in whom we feel sure that there is some impairment of brain functions but in whom the deficits are relatively mild. Further, lateralized disparities in sensory and motor functions will usually not be pronounced since, if they were, the indications of cerebral dysfunction would usually be more pronounced and then classified as more definite. This classification will be used principally to indicate the degree of over-all impairment rather than to indicate whether or not we would expect confirmation from physical neurological examination or history. This classification should not be used for patients in whom there is questionable or possible doubtful evidence of cerebral dysfunction. Patients in whom evidence of brain dysfunction is not fairly clear should be classified as no brain damage.

Definite: Patients will be assigned to this category when we feel strongly confident that there is impairment of cerebral functions or brain damage. Further, this category will be used for those subjects with brain damage who are more seriously impaired in their over-all adaptive capacities. Indications for classification of a patient in this category may depend upon pronounced lateralized deficits, but these should be supported by evidence of fairly serious impairment of adaptive abilities more generally.

Right hemisphere: This classification will be used when a patient presents compelling indications of involvement of the right hemisphere to a considerably greater degree than the left hemisphere. Although there may be one or two mild indications of left hemisphere dysfunction specifically, the preponderance of findings should implicate the right cerebral hemisphere. An impaired general level of performance, in association with mild signs of right-hemisphere dysfunction, should not necessarily provide evidence for use of this classification. A judgment will have to be made with respect to whether the general impairment shown by the patient could be caused by the indicated damage of the right cerebral hemisphere. If this judgment is positive, the right cerebral hemisphere classification should be used. However, even in the presence of strong signs of involvement of the right cerebral hemisphere, the presence of sufficient indications of left cerebral hemisphere damage or of sufficient general impairment that would seem unassociated with the lesion of the right cerebral hemisphere might be used as a basis for assigning the patient to another classification.

Right hemisphere diffuse: This classification will be used when there is inescapable evidence of diffuse involvement or involvement of the left cerebral hemisphere, except that the right cerebral hemisphere is clearly more damaged than the left.

Diffuse: This category will be used when there are no compelling indications of one hemisphere being more dysfunctional than the other, regardless of whether the general impairment is mild or severe. The signs of specific involvement of both cerebral hemispheres may even be quite pronounced provided they are about equally distributed to the 2 cerebral hemispheres.

Left hemisphere: The same types of criteria that apply to classification of a subject to the right cerebral hemisphere will apply for comparable findings relating to the left cerebral hemisphere. However, a lower verbal than performance IQ value will have to be considered with relation to the possible chronicity of brain dysfunction prior to using it as a compelling sign of left cerebral hemisphere dysfunction.

Left hemisphere diffuse: The criteria that apply in classification of a patient to the right hemisphere diffuse category will apply, except that the findings should relate to dysfunction of the left cerebral hemisphere.

Results of Factor Analysis of 79 Selected
Measures, Separately Computed for Retarded
Readers and Normal Readers

1. Factors are numbered according to the order of their appearance from the rotation (Varimax solution), with the subscript r denoting factors obtained from Retarded Readers and n denoting factors obtained from Normal Readers.

2. Factor loadings are reported to two decimal places, with decimal points omitted.

3. Factor loadings above .40 and below -.40 are underlined.

Factor Analysis, Retarded Readers, First 40 Measures, Factors 1-11

	Measure						*Factors and Loadings*					
		1r	2r	3r	4r	5r	6r	7r	8r	9r	10r	11r
1	Read. Achieve.	89	-03	-08	19	-03	11	-11	-11	05	-11	-02
2	Spell. Achieve.	91	00	08	06	01	01	01	07	05	-14	02
8	W-B Information	33	-53	-12	26	-03	-30	10	-11	-04	-19	08
9	W-B Comprehen.	08	-07	-13	14	-11	-15	-08	-20	02	-13	-22
10	W-B Digit Span	48	06	-13	05	-28	24	22	-05	-24	-47	08
11	W-B Arithmetic	55	-10	-12	-24	29	-09	13	-09	18	-15	02
12	W-B Similarities	-00	-43	-24	-12	-11	12	04	-26	-08	-15	-04
13	W-B Vocabulary	-00	-11	02	34	-21	-06	-15	-11	-10	-68	-11
14	W-B Pic. Arrange.	05	-88	-07	-14	10	06	-12	-02	-00	01	-08
15	W-B Pic. Complet.	11	-09	-24	15	-02	-04	-10	10	-12	-00	15
16	W-B Block Design	38	-44	17	18	37	23	14	-16	-09	12	16
17	W-B Object Assem.	18	07	01	09	04	08	-02	06	05	-05	-25
18	W-B Digit Symbol	55	-09	08	26	-03	-05	12	01	19	-05	16
19	Trail Making A	-37	07	34	-20	-14	-04	-18	-10	05	12	-30
20	Trail Making B	-57	15	08	-15	-21	19	-14	07	01	14	-37
21	Category	-13	23	-06	04	-08	-03	-15	-00	01	-24	14
22	Tact. Performance, preferred	12	01	-77	-13	-08	01	-06	-02	-16	05	-09
23	Tact. Performance, nonpreferred	04	-09	-83	12	04	-06	-09	01	12	-11	06
24	Tact. Performance, both	15	-10	-26	09	-23	-09	-09	01	19	-32	25
25	Tact. Performance, memory	14	-21	04	13	-03	06	-05	-05	01	01	03
26	Tact. Performance, location	21	-05	09	31	08	-06	-02	02	-52	-07	-07
27	Rhythm	44	-10	-08	16	01	04	-06	08	-45	-22	20
28	Speech Perception	-52	-04	-07	-27	-10	00	11	14	25	-19	03
29	Tapping, preferred	02	17	-21	73	09	-10	-07	11	-18	-07	10

30 Tapping, non-preferred	01	11	07	62	-16	-09	-11	04	-13	-09	06
33 Peabody Pic. Vocab., oral	09	-24	-10	53	-06	09	09	-14	09	-23	-12
35 Peabody Pic. Vocab., written	78	09	-23	25	-07	01	-07	-13	10	-04	01
36 Copy Square	07	-09	-08	20	-13	81	03	29	13	11	-13
37 Copy Cross	10	-20	02	26	-42	24	-02	-14	-04	-06	20
38 Copy Triangle	12	32	-27	42	29	10	-02	02	-32	02	00
39 Copy Key	16	-12	14	13	32	19	-05	-16	-28	-07	00
45 Finger Agn., rt.	-13	02	-13	-04	-12	-73	02	35	20	17	12
46 Finger Agn., lft.	16	-24	-13	-12	13	-49	14	09	-06	19	-06
47 Finger Writ., rt.	-26	-22	11	-10	-19	-12	19	04	07	33	-26
48 Finger Writ., lft.	-21	-16	-19	-25	17	-28	07	00	22	10	-16
49 Astereog., rt.	-15	-01	-11	03	08	-03	19	09	-04	-10	-09
50 Astereog., lft.	-08	-04	-21	03	04	-15	-06	-07	-05	08	-03
51 Hand Preference	25	06	-22	11	-00	13	-06	-16	17	12	-16
52 Eye Preference	-03	-07	-14	01	-03	04	-84	02	04	11	13
54 Grip Preference	21	-01	04	87	15	16	03	-11	-00	-08	-06

Factor Analysis, Retarded Readers, First 40 Measures, Factors 12-21

Factors and Loadings

Measure	12r	13r	14r	15r	16r	17r	18r	19r	20r	21r	Comm.
1 Read. Achieve.	02	09	15	-06	05	18	03	01	08	10	974
2 Spell. Achieve.	-03	-01	04	-05	-02	17	06	12	-04	13	929
8 W-B Information	22	-02	-04	09	27	01	09	32	-09	08	880
9 W-B Comprehen.	04	-13	-13	-03	71	00	13	07	-18	07	797
10 W-B Digit Span	11	-13	-05	-14	-10	07	11	-16	-24	16	900
11 W-B Arithmetic	28	15	-04	04	09	10	20	33	13	-01	843
12 W-B Similarities	10	-30	19	25	26	17	-42	05	10	14	870
13 W-B Vocabulary	-13	-06	-28	16	13	06	15	23	15	-02	935
14 W-B Pic. Arrange.	-02	03	-08	-10	03	06	02	13	-14	04	902
15 W-B Pic. Complet.	-02	15	-08	-06	78	10	-18	20	-03	10	883
16 W-B Block Design	02	03	06	-03	07	03	25	31	-16	15	894
17 W-B Object Assem.	03	-12	-13	-07	-01	08	10	05	-19	77	811
18 W-B Digit Symbol	19	-01	-01	-05	-02	49	04	22	-17	17	851
19 Trail Making A	-10	-36	-19	-12	-24	-28	-04	02	25	15	887
20 Trail Making B	06	-31	-15	07	-17	-23	-12	09	29	02	950
21 Category	-08	03	03	10	-19	-02	-02	-24	76	-09	871
22 Tact. Performance, preferred	-25	-13	-20	-19	16	03	-21	15	-05	03	919
23 Tact. Performance, nonpreferred	07	-07	-15	08	12	01	23	-11	10	-08	885
24 Tact. Performance, both	-28	13	-49	22	30	-16	-05	01	-15	-07	903
25 Tact. Performance, memory	07	12	11	-01	06	04	-01	83	-12	15	861
26 Tact. Performance, location	-04	08	07	-22	09	05	-04	54	-16	22	882
27 Rhythm	09	-32	-12	-34	10	-09	06	00	07	25	865
28 Speech Perception	-09	-14	-44	-01	-01	-09	-35	-08	-07	01	855
29 Tapping, preferred	-19	-18	11	06	-17	25	23	-05	07	19	953

30	Tapping, non-preferred	-25	-05	10	-10	07	<u>51</u>	-15	-03	21	19	929
33	Peabody Pic. Vocab., oral	-01	03	-15	16	06	24	33	35	12	22	871
35	Peabody Pic. Vocab., written	02	07	17	-05	01	22	17	00	-03	14	900
36	Copy Square	-01	02	12	01	-00	01	-01	-02	-01	04	879
37	Copy Cross	06	20	-12	-34	10	-23	07	02	-15	<u>42</u>	841
38	Copy Triangle	15	27	-16	28	17	13	10	-06	-16	00	839
39	Copy Key	07	09	19	-06	21	-10	02	15	-02	<u>61</u>	825
45	Finger Agn., rt.	-10	00	-06	-02	04	-09	10	-14	00	-<u>28</u>	914
46	Finger Agn., lft.	-26	15	-16	25	-13	-22	-11	-28	17	-23	853
47	Finger Writ., rt.	04	01	03	20	-<u>54</u>	-23	-33	07	09	-10	920
48	Finger Writ., lft.	04	-22	12	12	-<u>53</u>	-23	-37	05	-12	-09	930
49	Astereog., rt.	-08	-<u>86</u>	-17	02	<u>06</u>	-21	-01	-10	-07	-07	946
50	Astereog., lft.	03	-<u>15</u>	-<u>87</u>	04	11	-07	-03	-08	01	12	916
51	Hand Preference	37	-<u>48</u>	<u>03</u>	07	-31	06	11	-16	31	15	860
52	Eye Preference	-05	<u>09</u>	-04	08	08	13	-18	05	14	-11	870
54	Grip Preference	09	04	-03	-03	15	03	-05	09	-08	01	921

Factor Analysis, Retarded Readers, Final 39 Measures, Factors 1–11

		Factors and Loadings										
	Measure	1r	2r	3r	4r	5r	6r	7r	8r	9r	10r	11r
55	Grip, nonpreferred	20	-03	05	<u>90</u>	08	11	00	-12	05	-06	-07
56	Writing Speed, preferred	-25	-00	06	01	-01	13	11	09	00	-04	-<u>86</u>
57	Writing Speed, nonpreferred	08	-08	-10	14	04	05	12	-05	02	-04	-<u>77</u>
60	Sentence Repet.	-14	-01	05	-10	-03	-01	-11	03	00	<u>84</u>	<u>02</u>
62	Par. Comprehen.	-20	05	11	10	-06	03	-13	12	01	-<u>03</u>	-05
67	Oral Reading, sentences	-<u>87</u>	-04	16	-14	02	03	17	17	-07	07	-03
68	Articulation	-<u>33</u>	23	-21	-11	17	-01	<u>50</u>	19	19	28	-07
70	Serial Responses	-<u>85</u>	01	-01	04	-09	-02	-<u>10</u>	-02	23	-08	-02
73	Word Rhyming	<u>51</u>	-06	16	10	16	05	30	-05	-08	36	13
74	Express Ideas	-<u>01</u>	-04	-17	13	-13	06	02	-<u>78</u>	05	-03	18
75	Pic. Description	-09	-21	05	-07	13	11	<u>42</u>	-<u>24</u>	25	-01	-16
76	Sent. Formulation	-38	05	-20	-22	07	34	-<u>02</u>	-11	-07	-11	-02
77	Retell Paragraph	18	-06	14	12	18	-13	-01	-<u>76</u>	-05	-04	-15
78	Copy Figure	23	-35	24	32	05	37	-13	-<u>02</u>	01	06	16
79	Draw House	19	-17	-05	07	06	-07	12	-29	08	-02	18
80	Draw Man	11	00	04	-01	07	24	18	-03	-16	09	00
81	Draw Wheel	<u>48</u>	-07	-02	-04	-09	-15	20	-05	-38	-14	14
86	Words, Vis. Stim.	-<u>88</u>	04	09	-01	-01	-12	04	02	07	03	-02
87	Oral Spelling	<u>90</u>	-11	06	01	07	-00	-04	11	-09	-09	-04
88	Sent. Dictation	-<u>93</u>	01	01	-01	-09	-13	00	-01	-04	03	-01
91	Perceptual Speed, number	33	02	-03	04	04	-05	-02	04	05	-01	04
92	Perceptual Speed, form	<u>41</u>	01	-02	13	03	01	00	-03	-02	08	15
93	Perceptual Speed, nonsense letter	<u>64</u>	-10	28	18	03	02	13	-07	-02	05	02

	Measure											
94	Perceptual Speed, gestalt	19	-02	-02	34	30	-37	-36	-05	01	-25	16
95	Perceptual Speed, letter	54	-07	-04	18	-06	15	-12	-09	03	-03	13
96	Perceptual Speed, letter in syllable	56	-06	-09	15	13	-01	-09	-01	-12	-20	10
97	Perceptual Speed, two letters	50	-09	-06	05	12	26	-06	-03	07	-01	02
98	Perceptual Speed, form sequence	44	-06	20	04	01	13	03	07	-09	03	05
99	Perceptual Speed, nonsense syllable	65	-22	07	14	10	-06	23	-23	-26	11	04
100	Perceptual Speed, nonsense syllable	67	-32	11	07	-05	01	01	16	-16	14	02
101	Perceptual Speed, word	63	05	-01	-00	-00	-19	-08	-27	-16	-04	19
102	Perceptual Speed, word	58	02	09	22	08	-09	14	-28	34	08	25
103	Perceptual Speed, number	43	-03	-03	06	-07	06	-07	-05	-01	02	10
104	Spatial Orientation	-14	03	-04	04	-05	-07	-00	08	-02	13	-00
105	Reversals	-15	10	-01	-27	-70	09	-04	03	02	-18	-04
106	Word Association	-10	-10	-21	13	16	-15	06	34	-23	05	-05
108	Visual Spatial Memory	-37	30	-13	-21	-14	08	-07	42	-10	30	-14
109	Visual Temporal Memory	-19	29	01	-22	-51	-02	-16	10	01	24	07
	Age	43	07	-18	50	09	14	-13	-10	-10	-11	-07

Factor Analysis, Retarded Readers, Final 39 Measures, Factors 12-21

Factors and Loadings

	Measure	12r	13r	14r	15r	16r	17r	18r	19r	20r	21r	Comm.
55	Grip, nonpreferred	09	05	-01	-08	12	10	-13	06	-04	-00	956
56	Writing Speed, preferred	-04	-12	-17	-04	05	-16	-04	09	04	00	926
57	Writing Speed, nonpreferred	03	01	29	05	-05	-30	-09	-16	-23	07	933
60	Sentence Repet.	-03	03	-15	21	-14	07	11	-00	-13	-02	877
62	Par. Comprehen.	-03	02	-05	-04	-06	02	-82	-04	05	-16	815
67	Oral Reading, sentences	-05	04	-03	01	-02	-20	-10	07	11	-01	935
68	Articulation	-16	-14	16	29	-15	-07	-24	05	-02	07	906
70	Serial Responses	-07	14	08	-06	-11	-02	10	08	-07	08	875
73	Word Rhyming	15	09	33	-29	20	-07	-04	10	09	-03	873
74	Express Ideas	-22	13	11	-02	24	09	03	15	-10	07	889
75	Pic. Description	00	-21	10	05	56	12	-02	-05	02	08	801
76	Sent. Formulation	-02	-36	-22	01	35	-03	05	49	-08	-13	951
77	Retell Paragraph	17	-04	-21	06	-02	-06	16	-03	12	20	882
78	Copy Figure	-22	-11	20	11	-22	05	39	-03	16	19	907
79	Draw House	-10	-05	-08	03	-07	-22	03	-02	09	75	867
80	Draw Man	20	19	-01	-08	26	02	13	21	06	73	896
81	Draw Wheel	14	-08	05	-24	07	-17	37	11	05	12	774
86	Words, Vis. Stim.	-04	02	04	-09	11	-18	06	08	14	-18	922

87	Oral Spelling	-09	-00	02	-04	-05	22	11	09	10	04	957
88	Sent. Dictation	-04	-07	02	05	-08	-10	-12	-07	03	-08	938
91	Perceptual Speed, number	13	-01	-01	07	05	88	-10	03	04	-07	939
92	Perceptual Speed, form	08	09	-01	10	02	82	-02	-05	04	-14	929
93	Perceptual Speed, nonsense letter	-01	19	05	-02	19	48	15	19	02	-02	927
94	Perceptual Speed, gestalt	12	-00	17	-03	29	00	06	23	-10	-15	818
95	Perceptual Speed, letter	-03	06	05	03	06	73	01	01	-01	05	948
96	Perceptual Speed, letter in syllable	-14	16	10	-10	-01	58	15	25	-11	-01	936
97	Perceptual Speed, two letters	19	17	-08	-22	18	60	17	13	-06	-00	916
98	Perceptual Speed, form sequence	68	10	05	-05	01	26	-01	18	-14	19	904
99	Perceptual Speed, nonsense syllable	11	-02	03	-04	08	41	-11	14	04	05	913
100	Perceptual Speed, nonsense syllable	17	04	-09	04	16	42	03	05	-12	22	949
101	Perceptual Speed, word	12	28	-21	-14	24	26	-09	11	-18	15	939
102	Perceptual Speed, word	23	-04	-26	-09	-08	24	08	16	-07	07	919
103	Perceptual Speed, number	-05	04	09	-01	04	80	05	-04	-06	-07	883
104	Spatial Orientation	-03	01	-17	89	-03	04	11	-02	05	-06	894
105	Reversals	-02	12	01	12	12	04	-04	-01	03	-29	776
106	Word Association	-07	08	-27	-64	10	05	13	05	-08	05	837
108	Visual Spatial Memory	-19	06	-15	09	05	-20	-36	03	11	-03	870
109	Visual Temporal Memory	03	-15	03	31	-09	-03	-27	13	31	-17	870
	Age	08	-04	-23	-04	19	29	20	40	09	09	956

Factor Analysis, Normal Readers, First 40 Measures, Factors 1-12

Factors and Loadings

	Measure	1n	2n	3n	4n	5n	6n	7n	8n	9n	10n	11n	12n
1	Read. Achieve.	84	-27	12	02	01	05	09	-08	-15	02	17	00
2	Spell. Achieve.	87	-14	06	17	-02	-06	16	06	-18	20	07	08
8	W-B Information	73	-26	-10	06	09	-01	-18	17	18	-00	02	09
9	W-B Comprehen.	38	-22	39	-03	26	-01	-01	07	02	-22	09	-04
10	W-B Digit Span	44	-13	-01	33	20	-19	13	04	-42	-10	19	-02
11	W-B Arithmetic	52	-12	-04	04	10	00	06	04	-07	-03	19	08
12	W-B Similarities	35	-14	-14	-01	-07	02	-17	12	07	30	13	27
13	W-B Vocabulary	82	-11	-01	08	08	-09	13	07	07	-14	-07	03
14	W-B Pic. Arrange.	33	-09	-24	-37	-08	-18	02	-07	-51	09	-12	04
15	W-B Pic. Complet.	16	-06	-12	-08	07	14	16	10	-18	-04	03	03
16	W-B Block Design	03	-13	-24	21	08	-47	01	16	-01	-27	13	-14
17	W-B Object Assem.	07	-06	-84	-13	11	-06	04	07	-14	01	10	06

18	W-B Digit Symbol	22	-65	-10	-11	-03	09	12	15	10	-10	13	-04
19	Trail Making A	-09	20	-01	25	-28	-20	-15	07	-23	-08	-01	-29
20	Trail Making B	-20	22	10	-04	-10	-04	01	-06	21	-10	-02	-04
21	Category	-27	12	04	-25	-25	-05	-07	02	01	01	-70	02
22	Tact. Performance, preferred	26	-05	-18	11	-15	04	09	-14	08	29	-08	42
23	Tact. Performance, nonpreferred	15	14	20	-07	-73	-02	-29	09	09	-03	06	28
24	Tact. Performance, both	06	-03	02	14	-85	03	03	11	-02	-03	11	-05
25	Tact. Performance, memory	28	-09	-00	05	65	10	-10	21	-16	-02	22	-05
26	Tact. Performance, location	45	-01	11	17	61	19	-10	10	-07	02	14	-20
27	Rhythm	18	-09	-11	-28	-13	-22	06	-06	-15	-03	76	12
28	Speech Perception	-44	-16	06	-41	-07	-13	-14	08	-14	-08	-14	-25
29	Tapping, preferred	45	-38	-12	07	-24	20	04	-08	-11	-20	24	-01
30	Tapping, non-preferred	59	-24	-18	-09	-08	21	03	01	-10	-30	14	08
33	Peabody Pic. Vocab., oral	86	-16	-08	-07	-09	02	-21	19	09	16	-02	-06
35	Peabody Pic. Vocab., written	83	-15	-09	-17	21	-01	-10	00	06	-23	07	10
36	Copy Square	-31	-01	-14	-20	-15	-31	-10	-31	06	-20	-28	18
37	Copy Cross	26	-26	-11	04	06	-44	04	01	-19	-01	-07	-05
38	Copy Triangle	-13	-09	-04	-79	06	06	-03	-28	-06	04	09	-15
39	Copy Key	-23	07	-17	-04	-32	-19	-48	-09	05	-19	-02	-09
45	Finger Agn., rt.	-05	-10	02	-09	-06	-02	-00	-03	23	-04	-02	04
46	Finger Agn., lft.	-03	-13	04	-00	-18	05	09	-20	80	-02	-10	-09
47	Finger Writ., rt.	-17	10	14	-11	04	46	-03	-76	13	04	03	01
48	Finger Writ., lft.	-15	26	-00	-15	01	07	-08	-82	09	-03	05	-09
49	Astereog., rt.	-05	-06	-21	-14	11	-03	00	-15	07	08	-24	-66
50	Astereog., lft.	-14	-01	12	-08	10	-03	03	-03	08	17	01	-82
51	Hand Preference	-00	-27	-10	-04	-09	01	-15	-02	26	-01	-02	13
52	Eye Preference	-04	06	15	-13	16	12	-01	-03	03	08	00	-24
54	Grip Preference	57	-27	-00	-12	11	48	10	06	02	-31	03	-01

Factor Analysis, Normal Readers, First 40 Measures, Factors 13-23

Factors and Loadings

	Measure	13n	14n	15n	16n	17n	18n	19n	20n	21n	22n	23n	Comm.
1	Read. Achieve.	10	03	-10	-06	-07	03	04	01	-08	-10	-04	911
2	Spell. Achieve.	06	09	03	06	08	02	04	06	-11	-04	05	959
8	W-B Information	06	-10	03	01	-04	01	00	11	12	-09	-30	864
9	W-B Comprehen.	-06	-26	07	20	-05	47	02	18	03	-06	16	864
10	W-B Digit Span	-06	27	-05	04	-16	24	14	-31	-03	05	-16	946
11	W-B Arithmetic	09	19	-13	36	02	12	-25	03	44	-09	-18	845
12	W-B Similarities	09	-02	05	09	04	69	-03	12	03	-01	-10	926
13	W-B Vocabulary	03	-07	05	17	-08	22	01	03	22	-01	08	905
14	W-B Pic. Arrange.	-07	-00	14	20	-24	-09	-17	03	-16	-02	-02	826
15	W-B Pic. Complet.	-08	-08	15	02	-03	83	-19	-11	06	-10	10	939
16	W-B Block Design	-35	-00	02	33	06	17	-14	02	-35	01	-20	917
17	W-B Object Assem.	-08	-05	-04	05	-03	16	-00	19	-12	-02	05	881

#	Measure												
18	W-B Digit Symbol	11	-15	14	20	-16	14	16	20	-11	-08	-21	838
19	Trail Making A	-18	32	-01	-60	-02	-06	09	07	01	05	16	941
20	Trail Making B	02	02	10	-77	09	-11	17	-19	-02	09	13	886
21	Category	-07	11	10	-06	06	-01	17	08	13	-08	-00	804
22	Tact. Performance, preferred	-36	-20	14	-09	-18	02	14	24	06	11	-13	780
23	Tact. Performance, nonpreferred	08	-13	-09	-09	-09	08	04	-01	-21	12	-15	929
24	Tact. Performance, both	-36	02	01	-04	07	-07	-04	16	03	07	-02	939
25	Tact. Performance, memory	-13	-09	-05	09	15	14	-09	-00	-12	13	-33	877
26	Tact. Performance, location	-14	-03	-17	08	16	-02	08	-14	-12	-14	-26	947
27	Rhythm	-07	02	07	-06	10	16	-09	-01	13	02	-12	905
28	Speech Perception	-24	-03	07	41	09	-12	14	-15	03	-06	05	848
29	Tapping, preferred	01	-22	01	39	-17	02	19	-16	-31	-02	05	973
30	Tapping, non-preferred	07	-29	03	17	-13	05	06	-23	-13	08	24	890
33	Peabody Pic. Vocab., oral	02	-12	-17	01	02	04	04	-12	-01	-02	04	957
35	Peabody Pic. Vocab., written	-05	-05	-08	-06	-02	05	06	06	12	04	-04	914
36	Copy Square	-16	-32	-09	-10	08	-15	00	00	-03	-07	-46	928
37	Copy Cross	20	-06	-04	-10	-06	-11	-11	-15	-62	-16	-05	918
38	Copy Triangle	-02	-01	09	-04	-03	04	-06	01	04	12	-03	805
39	Copy Key	16	-06	-11	02	-00	19	-05	08	-39	-07	-38	900
45	Finger Agn., rt.	-04	07	90	-07	-03	10	09	-01	-04	00	-05	921
46	Finger Agn., lft.	05	25	18	-15	-00	-16	-14	05	05	09	-04	942
47	Finger Writ., rt.	03	01	03	-08	00	-10	00	-12	-07	-17	02	950
48	Finger Writ., lft.	07	11	-01	01	-02	-10	11	-01	04	22	06	907
49	Astereog., rt.	02	15	36	02	-03	-03	-05	-04	21	22	-26	934
50	Astereog., lft.	-04	02	-11	-12	09	-12	13	-07	-23	-02	21	931
51	Hand Preference	-17	28	-57	-01	-14	-14	21	-28	07	-16	-21	866
52	Eye Preference	03	-01	-12	-08	20	07	01	-78	-04	-04	-12	840
54	Grip Preference	-04	-01	-00	15	-21	25	02	-20	-06	08	10	954

Factor Analysis, Normal Readers, Final 39 Measures, Factors 1-12

Measure	Factors and Loadings											
	1n	2n	3n	4n	5n	6n	7n	8n	9n	10n	11n	12n
55 Grip, nonpreferred	52	-22	-01	-13	08	53	13	-01	04	-28	07	04
56 Writing Speed, preferred	-22	58	-07	00	04	-00	-31	-04	-02	12	-11	03
57 Writing Speed, nonpreferred	-08	24	-05	-06	-09	04	-38	-45	04	10	-29	15
60 Sentence Repet.	-58	-01	19	-14	10	-18	04	-09	06	23	-24	04
62 Par. Comprehen.	-11	-06	-01	-11	-10	02	04	-06	04	01	08	-04
67 Oral Reading, sentences	06	-22	06	-04	08	83	-01	-21	13	-00	-14	05
68 Articulation	-36	05	06	20	12	-23	01	08	-02	11	-27	-26
70 Serial Responses	-34	25	-10	-18	26	11	42	-05	-00	00	22	-27
73 Word Rhyming	37	02	-22	16	-04	03	23	-22	-17	-03	-06	18
74 Express Ideas	11	-08	-23	27	03	54	14	-22	-12	-06	10	-20

75	Pic. Description	-38	-07	07	09	-26	02	-08	21	-26	16	-27	-22
76	Sent. Formulation	07	03	02	04	-06	04	-02	01	09	-91	02	14
77	Retell Paragraph	21	10	-21	-52	-11	14	-33	36	-09	-08	-11	23
78	Copy Figure	12	-25	-22	-02	09	-13	-04	07	-37	-11	22	-16
79	Draw House	-11	04	-04	-08	-01	02	00	09	02	-05	20	08
80	Draw Man	-21	-10	-07	04	02	03	05	00	-20	06	05	-08
81	Draw Wheel	11	-14	-01	-02	01	-07	-04	13	-24	-12	08	09
86	Words, Vis. Stim.	-14	14	-04	-08	-08	00	07	06	07	-07	03	-02
87	Oral Spelling	78	-16	13	07	-08	-05	17	-06	-27	19	04	06
88	Sent. Dictation	-49	38	-12	-12	-08	17	-38	35	-00	-06	-22	-18
91	Perceptual Speed, number	12	-91	04	-07	-10	-06	05	-01	09	-02	-03	01
92	Perceptual Speed, form	22	-80	02	10	-02	19	-22	-01	-04	01	12	-00
93	Perceptual Speed, nonsense letter	08	-52	-15	-02	-13	01	21	14	03	-04	04	-16
94	Perceptual Speed, gestalt	02	-44	-28	-02	07	-05	-22	27	-15	-01	23	17
95	Perceptual Speed, letter	18	-85	00	-03	-03	13	23	08	-02	02	-09	-03
96	Perceptual Speed, letter in syllable	25	·70	-09	-05	12	13	-05	10	01	-10	-05	-26
97	Perceptual Speed, two letters	19	-79	-16	-23	06	02	03	08	-12	-04	21	14
98	Perceptual Speed, form sequence	14	-26	-03	01	00	-08	-01	-05	-09	21	-04	09
99	Perceptual Speed, nonsense syllable	16	-62	05	20	06	-23	-24	-00	-12	16	-13	-10
100	Perceptual Speed, nonsense syllable	01	-67	-11	17	26	-35	14	-12	10	19	19	07
101	Perceptual Speed, word	25	-63	16	12	28	-02	12	-19	-06	09	-01	08
102	Perceptual Speed, word	23	-38	-19	21	-04	05	63	21	07	-02	07	02
103	Perceptual Speed, number	18	-83	05	03	07	16	-05	21	-09	02	-04	02
104	Spatial Orientation	20	11	44	-32	06	32	-09	-10	14	09	-08	19
105	Reversals	02	04	25	-01	02	02	-01	-11	70	-14	-06	06
106	Word Association	28	-27	36	-22	-03	-11	11	-10	-53	-04	10	33
108	Visual Spatial Memory	-27	17	-05	-49	-05	11	-06	08	12	-08	-14	-17
109	Visual Temporal Memory	-21	-02	-05	00	-15	21	03	-09	11	01	-11	-09
	Age	71	-38	06	04	-05	23	10	20	-13	-06	01	11

Factor Analysis, Normal Readers, Final 39 Measures, Factors 12-23

		Factors and Loadings											
	Measure	13n	14n	15n	16n	17n	18n	19n	20n	21n	22n	23n	Comm.
55	Grip, nonpreferred	05	-05	-01	16	-23	19	02	-21	03	11	19	931
56	Writing Speed, preferred	-28	04	-28	21	-24	-01	-03	-15	07	-03	11	817
57	Writing Speed, nonpreferred	-46	13	-13	01	-25	-07	-04	04	04	-06	-16	894

60	Sentence Repet.	11	25	-27	-04	-13	-05	13	01	-20	-06	04	786
62	Par. Comprehen.	06	-07	06	-10	-02	-10	-13	06	-03	91	11	953
67	Oral Reading, sentences	-00	08	-01	02	16	05	-06	01	06	-01	09	887
68	Articulation	11	-03	-12	41	10	07	24	14	-18	12	37	875
70	Serial Responses	10	-04	27	-10	-01	-16	27	29	-24	08	-11	947
73	Word Rhyming	-04	-37	02	-10	22	00	19	-12	-38	-26	19	876
74	Express Ideas	-09	-11	-43	11	05	38	00	-00	-08	-01	09	946
75	Pic. Description	-28	08	-06	17	24	16	20	-16	13	03	23	809
76	Sent. Formulation	-05	-11	05	-09	17	-05	-04	11	04	-03	-07	942
77	Retell Paragraph	03	-03	02	25	07	36	-03	-09	05	02	-11	940
78	Copy Figure	06	-13	37	01	03	33	-35	08	-08	-30	05	869
79	Draw House	-01	00	-05	14	-09	19	-83	00	-25	19	-03	927
80	Draw Man	-02	-02	08	09	05	-03	-24	-03	-85	08	10	919
81	Draw Wheel	-09	-84	-01	10	-04	12	-01	-01	-09	10	00	898
86	Words, Vis. Stim.	-92	-08	-02	-04	-04	04	-01	05	03	-06	08	946
87	Oral Spelling	11	10	07	-03	05	01	05	-17	-03	-22	-15	951
88	Sent. Dictation	03	03	-10	-14	-05	-07	03	-06	04	04	-05	853
91	Perceptual Speed, number	-00	-06	-07	-01	-06	14	01	-05	-02	01	11	917
92	Perceptual Speed, form	-04	-04	26	08	-02	-03	04	14	03	06	11	902
93	Perceptual Speed, nonsense letter	07	17	-15	10	-13	27	32	43	14	-05	-05	875
94	Perceptual Speed, gestalt	-12	28	05	13	-34	12	06	-30	-13	13	-12	894
95	Perceptual Speed, letter	04	-03	-12	09	-14	-09	-18	-11	-00	-05	12	952
96	Perceptual Speed, letter in syllable	23	15	-10	30	-16	16	-12	02	-07	-05	-04	927
97	Perceptual Speed, two letters	11	01	-03	06	15	13	10	-00	-05	08	-08	910
98	Perceptual Speed, form sequence	-07	-03	-01	03	-84	00	-07	21	04	03	-01	917
99	Perceptual Speed, nonsense syllable	-10	-27	-06	17	-12	10	-03	-02	10	36	00	904
100	Perceptual Speed, nonsense syllable	06	-05	-10	-17	-09	-02	-01	-13	-16	-09	-06	905
101	Perceptual Speed, word	18	20	12	21	28	-01	10	09	-07	05	-07	873
102	Perceptual Speed, word	-09	04	-08	09	-02	23	-05	-01	-13	03	02	833
103	Perceptual Speed, number	-15	-07	02	-05	-12	-12	-07	-14	01	-01	-07	901
104	Spatial Orientation	-10	-06	03	-18	34	-13	29	08	09	-03	31	909
105	Reversals	-22	19	16	-00	06	02	18	-05	33	-05	20	895
106	Word Association	18	19	-02	-20	-03	05	11	-08	-06	02	01	895
108	Visual Spatial Memory	-20	01	-05	08	01	10	-01	65	08	11	05	939
109	Visual Temporal Memory	-10	-07	-03	-18	04	07	-00	15	-11	11	83	939
	Age	-02	04	12	02	-08	19	-12	07	-02	21	-14	931

Bibliography

Altus, Grace T. A WISC profile for retarded readers. *Journal of Consulting Psychology*, 1956, 20, 155-156.

Anastasi, Anne. *Differential Psychology*. 3rd ed. New York: Macmillan, 1958.

Anderson, A.L. The effect of laterality localization of focal brain lesions on the Wechsler-Bellevue subtests. *Journal of Clinical Psychology*, 1951, 7, 149-153.

Bauer, R.W., and Becka, D.M. Intellect after cerebral vascular accident. *Journal of Nervous and Mental Disease*, 1954, 120, 379-384.

Belmont, Lillian, and Birch, H.G. Lateral dominance, lateral awareness, and reading disability. *Child Development*, 1965, 36, 57-71.

Bender, Lauretta. A visual-motor test and its clinical use. *American Journal of Orthopsychiatry Monograph*, 1938, No. 3.

Benton, A.L. *Right-left Discrimination and Finger Localization*. New York: Hoeber, 1959.

_____. Behavioral indices of brain injury in children. *Child Development*, 1962, 33, 199-208.

BIMD Computer Programs Manual. Division of Biostatistics, Department of Preventive Medicine and Public Health, University of California Medical School, Los Angeles, 1961.

Birch, H.G. Dyslexia and the maturation of visual function, in *Reading Disability*, ed. J. Money. Baltimore: Johns Hopkins Press, 1962.

Boring, E.G. *A History of Experimental Psychology*. rev. ed. New York: Appleton-Century-Crofts, 1950.

Brain, W.R. *Speech Disorders*. London: Butterworth, 1961.

Bruner, J.S., Goodnow, Jacqueline, and Austin, G.A. *A Study of Thinking*. New York: John Wiley, 1956.

Burks, H.F., and Bruce, P. The characteristics of poor and good readers as disclosed by the Wechsler Intelligence Scale for Children. *Journal of Educational Psychology*, 1955, 46, 488-493.

Carter, R.P. A descriptive analysis of the adult adjustment of persons once identified as disabled readers. Unpublished doctoral dissertation, Indiana University, 1964.

Cattell, R.B. *Factor Analysis*. New York: Harper, 1952.

Cherry, C. *On Human Communication*. Cambridge: Technology Press, 1957.

Coan, R.W. Facts, factors, and artifacts: The quest for psychological meaning. *Psychological Review*, 1964, 71, 123-140.

Cohn, R. Delayed acquisition of reading and writing abilities in children. *Archives of Neurology*, 1961, 4, 153-164.

Costa, L.D., and Vaughan, H.G. Performance of patients with lateralized cerebral lesions. I. Verbal and perceptual tests. *Journal of Nervous and Mental Disease*, 1962, 134, 162-168.

Critchley, M. *Developmental Dyslexia*. London: Heinemann, 1964.

de Hirsch, Katrina. Gestalt psychology as applied to language disturbances. *Journal of Nervous and Mental Disease,* 1954, 120, 257-261.

_____. Prediction of future reading disabilities in children with oral language disorders. *Folia Phoniatrica,* 1955, 7, 235-250.

_____. Tests designed to discover potential reading difficulties at the six-year-old level. *American Journal of Orthopsychiatry,* 1957, 27, 566-576.

Doehring, D.G. The validity of intelligence tests for evaluating deaf children. *Journal of Speech and Hearing Disorders,* 1965, 30, 299-300.

_____, and Lacy, Julia. *Programmed Instruction in Beginning Reading.* Indiana University Medical Center (mimeo.), 1963.

_____, Reitan, R.M., and Kløve, H. Changes in patterns of intelligence test performance associated with homonymous visual field defects. *Journal of Nervous and Mental Disease,* 1961, 132, 227-233.

Donaldson, R.W. Experiments in reading nonvisual text. *Quarterly Progress Report No. 79, Research Laboratory of Electronics, Massachusetts Institute of Technology,* 1965, 237-244.

Drew, A.L. A neurological appraisal of familial congenital word-blindness. *Brain,* 1956, 79, 440-460.

Dunn, L.M. *Peabody Picture Vocabulary Test.* Minneapolis: American Guidance Service, 1959.

Farrant, R.H. The intellective abilities of deaf and hearing children compared by factor analysis. *American Annals of the Deaf,* 1964, 109, 306-325.

Ferguson, G.A. On learning and human ability. *Canadian Journal of Psychology,* 1954, 8, 95-112.

Gagné, R.M. The acquisition of knowledge. *Psychological Review,* 1962, 69, 355-365.

Gaito, J., and Zavala, A. Neurochemistry and learning. *Psychological Bulletin,* 1964, 61, 45-62.

Geschwind, N. The anatomy of acquired disorders of reading, in *Reading Disability,* ed. J. Money. Baltimore: Johns Hopkins Press, 1962.

Goldiamond, I. Indicators of perception: I. Subliminal perception, subception, unconscious perception: An analysis in terms of psychophysical indicator methodology. *Psychological Bulletin,* 1958, 55, 373-411.

Goodenough, Florence L. *Measurement of Intelligence by Drawings.* New York: Harcourt, Brace, 1926.

Graham, E.E., and Kamano, D. Reading failure as a factor in the WAIS subtest patterns of youthful offenders. *Journal of Clinical Psychology,* 1958, 14, 302-305.

Guilford, J.P. The structure of intellect. *Psychological Bulletin,* 1956, 53, 267-293.

_____. Frontiers in thinking that teachers should know about. *Reading Teacher,* 1960, 15, 176-182.

Hallgren, B. Specific dyslexia ("congenital word-blindness"): A clinical and genetic study. *Acta Psychiatrica Neurologica,* Supplement 65, 1950.

Halstead, W.C. *Brain and Intelligence.* Chicago: University of Chicago Press, 1947.

_____, and Wepman, J.M. The Halstead-Wepman aphasia screening test. *Journal of Speech and Hearing Disorders,* 1949, 14, 9-15.

Harris, A.J. *Harris Tests of Lateral Dominance, Manual of Directions for Administration and Interpretation.* New York: The Psychological Corporation, 1947.

_____. Lateral dominance, directional confusion, and reading disability. *Journal of Psychology,* 1957, 44, 283-294.

_____. *How to Increase Reading Ability.* 4th ed. New York: McKay, 1961.
Head, H. *Aphasia and Kindred Disorders of Speech.* New York: Macmillan, 1926.
Hebb, D.O. *Organization of Behavior.* New York: John Wiley, 1949.
_____. Intelligence, brain function and the theory of mind. *Brain,* 1959, 82, 260-275.
_____. Distinctive features of learning in the higher animal, in *Brain Mechanisms and Learning,* ed. J. F. Delafresnaye. Oxford: Blackwell, 1961. (a)
_____. On the meaning of objective psychology. *Transactions of the Royal Society of Canada.* 1961, 55, 81-86. (b)
_____. The semiautonomous process: Its nature and nurture. *American Psychologist,* 1963, 18, 16-27.
Heilbrun, A.B. Psychological test performance as a function of lateral localization of cerebral lesion. *Journal of Comparative and Physiological Psychology,* 1956, 49, 10-14.
Heimburger, R.F., and Reitan, R.M. Easily administered written test for lateralizing brain lesions. *Journal of Neurosurgery,* 1961, 18, 301-312.
Hermann, K. *Reading Disability: A Medical Study of Word-Blindness and Related Handicaps.* Springfield, Ill.: Charles C. Thomas, 1959.
Hinshelwood, J. *Congenital Word Blindness.* London: H.K. Lewis, 1917.
Hively, W. Confessions of an experimental analyst of early reading behavior. Paper read at the American Educational Research Association. February, 1964.
Howes, D.H. On the interpretation of word frequency as a variable affecting speed of recognition. *Journal of Experimental Psychology,* 1954, 48, 106-112.

Jasper, H.H., Proctor, L.D., Knighton, R.S., Noshay, W.C., and Costello, R.T., eds. *Reticular Formation of the Brain.* Boston: Little, Brown, 1958.
Jastak, J. *Wide Range Achievement Test.* Wilmington, Del.: C.L. Story, 1946.
Johnson, Marjorie. Factors related to disability in reading. *Journal of Experimental Education,* 1957, 26, 1-26.

Kawi, A.A., and Pasamanick, B. Prenatal and perinatal factors in the development of childhood reading disorders. *Monographs of the Society for Research in Child Development,* 1959, 24, no. 4.
Kinsbourne, M., and Warrington, Elizabeth K. Developmental factors in reading and writing backwardness. *British Journal of Psychology,* 1963, 54, 145-156.
Kløve, H. Relationship of differential electroencephalographic patterns to distribution of Wechsler-Bellevue scores. *Neurology,* 1959, 9, 871-876.
_____, and Reitan, R.M. Effect of dysphasia and spatial distortion on Wechsler-Bellevue results. *Archives of Neurology and Psychiatry,* 1958, 80, 708-713.
Kolers, P.A., Eden, M., and Boyer, Ann. Reading as a perceptual skill. *Quarterly Progress Report No. 74, Research Laboratory of Electronics, Massachusetts Institute of Technology,* 1964, 214-217.

Lachman, F.M. Perceptual-motor development in children retarded in reading ability. *Journal of Consulting Psychology,* 1960, 24, 427-431.
Lashley, K.S. The problem of serial order in behavior, in *Cerebral Mechanisms in Behavior,* ed. L. A. Jeffress. New York: John Wiley, 1951.

McFie, J. Recent advances in phrenology. *The Lancet,* August, 1961, 360-363.
_____, and Piercy, M.F. Intellectual impairment with localized cerebral lesions. *Brain,* 1952, 75, 292-311.
Matthews, C.G., and Reitan, R.M. Correlations of Wechsler-Bellevue rank orders of subtest means in lateralized and non-lateralized brain-damaged groups. *Perceptual and Motor Skills,* 1964, 19, 391-399.

Miller, G.A., Galanter, E., and Pribram, K.H. *Plans and the Structure of Behavior,* New York: Henry Holt, 1960.

Milner, Brenda. Laterality effects in audition, in *Interhemispheric Relations and Cerebral Dominance,* ed. V. B. Mountcastle. Baltimore: Johns Hopkins Press, 1962.

_____. Psychological defects produced by temporal lobe excision. *Research Publications of the Association for Research in Nervous and Mental Diseases,* 1958, 36, 244-257.

Milner, P.M. The Cell Assembly: Mark II. *Psychological Review,* 1957, 64, 242-252.

Money, J., ed. *Reading Disability.* Baltimore: Johns Hopkins Press, 1962.

Morrow, R.S., and Mark, J.C. The correlation of intelligence and neurological findings on twenty-two patients autopsied for brain damage. *Journal of Consulting Psychology,* 1955, 19, 282-289.

Muehl, S., Knott, J.R., and Benton, A.L. EEG abnormality and psychological test performance in reading disability. *Cortex,* 1965, 1, 434-440.

Myklebust, H.R. *Development and Disorders of Written Language.* Vol. I.: Picture Story Test. New York: Grune and Stratton, 1965.

_____, and Johnson, Doris. Dyslexia in children. *Exceptional Children,* 1962, 29, 14-25.

Neville, D. A comparison of the WISC patterns of male retarded and nonretarded readers. *Journal of Educational Research,* 1961, 54, 195-197.

Orton, S.T. *Reading, Writing and Speech Problems in Children.* New York: W.W. Norton, 1937.

Osgood, C.E., and Miron, M.S., eds. *Approaches to the Study of Aphasia.* Urbana: University of Illinois Press, 1963.

Overall, J.E. Note on the scientific status of factors. *Psychological Bulletin,* 1964, 61, 270-276.

Rabinovitch, R.D., Drew, A.L., De Jong, R.N., Ingram, W., and Withey, L. A research approach to reading retardation. *Research Publications of the Association for Research in Nervous and Mental Diseases,* 1954, 34, 363-396.

Reed, H.B., and Reitan, R.M. Intelligence test performances of brain-damaged subjects with lateralized motor deficits. *Journal of Consulting Psychology,* 1963, 27, 102-106.

Reitan, R.M. Investigation of the validity of Halstead's measures of biological intelligence. *Archives of Neurology and Psychiatry,* 1955, 73, 28-35.

_____. Certain differential effects of left and right cerebral lesions in human adults. *Journal of Comparative and Physiological Psychology,* 1955, 48, 474-477.

_____. The validity of the Trail Making Test as an indicator of organic brain damage. *Perceptual and Motor Skills,* 1958, 8, 271-276.

_____. *The Effects of Brain Lesions on Adaptive Abilities in Human Beings.* Indiana University Medical Center (mimeo.), 1959.

_____. Psychological deficits resulting from cerebral lesions in man, in *The Frontal Granular Cortex and Behavior,* ed. J. M. Warren and K. A. Akert. New York: McGraw-Hill, 1964.

_____. A research program on the psychological effects of brain lesions in human beings, in *International Review of Research in Mental Retardation,* ed. R. N. Ellis. New York: Academic Press, 1965.

Robeck, Mildred. Subtest patterning of problem readers on the WISC. *California Journal of Educational Research,* 1960, 11, 110-115.

Schuell, Hildred, and Jenkins, J.J.   The nature of language deficit in aphasia. *Psychological Review,* 1959, 66, 45-67.

_____, _____, and Jimenez-Pabon, E. *Aphasia in Adults.* New York: Harper and Row, 1964.

Shankweiler, D. Developmental dyslexia: A critique and review of recent evidence. *Cortex,* 1964, 1, 53-62.

_____. A study of developmental dyslexia. *Neuropsychologia,* 1964, 1, 267-286.

Sheldon, M.S., and Garton, Jeanette.   A note on "A WISC profile for retarded readers." *Alberta Journal of Educational Research,* 1959, 5, 264-267.

Silver, A.A., and Hagin, Rosa. Specific reading disability: Delineation of the syndrome and relationship to cerebral dominance. *Comprehensive Psychiatry,* 1960, 1, 126-134.

_____. Specific reading disability: Follow-up studies. *American Journal of Orthopsychiatry,* 1964, 34, 95-102.

Skinner, B.F. The science of learning and the art of teaching. *Harvard Educational Review,* 1954, 24, 86-97.

Smith, D.E.P., and Carrigan, Patricia. *The Nature of Reading Disability.* New York: Harcourt, Brace, 1959.

Spearman, C. *The Abilities of Man.* New York: Macmillan, 1927.

Spitzer, R.L., Rabkin, R., and Kramer, Y. The relationship between "mixed dominance" and reading disabilities. *Journal of Pediatrics,* 1959, 54, 76-80.

Staats, A.W., Minke, K.A., Finley, J.R., Wolf, M., and Brooks, L.D. A reinforcer system and experimental procedure for the laboratory study of reading acquisition. *Child Development,* 1964, 35, 209-231.

Stark, R. An investigation of unilateral cerebral pathology with equated verbal and visual-spatial tasks. *Journal of Abnormal and Social Psychology,* 1961, 62, 282-287.

Teuber, H.L. Some observations on the organization of higher functions after penetrating brain injury in man, in *The Biology of Mental Health and Disease.* New York: Hoeber-Harper, 1952.

Thurstone, L.L. Primary mental abilities. *Psychometric Monographs,* 1938, No. 1.

Tomkins, C. The last skill acquired. *The New Yorker,* 1963, 39, 127-157.

Vernon, M.D. *Backwardness in Reading.* Cambridge: Cambridge University Press, 1957.

Walker, Helen, and Lev, J. *Statistical Inference.* New York: Henry Holt, 1953.

Wechsler, D. *The Measurement of Adult Intelligence.* 3rd ed. Baltimore: Williams & Wilkins, 1944.

Wepman, J.M. Dyslexia, language, and concept formation, in *Reading Disability,* ed. J. Money. Baltimore: Johns Hopkins Press, 1962.

Wheeler, L., and Reitan, R.M. Presence and laterality of brain damage predicted from responses to a short aphasia screening test. *Perceptual and Motor Skills,* 1962, 15, 783-799.

Index

Abilities, 2-4

Age: of retarded readers, 17; distributions, 20, 21; related to pattern of impairment, 142

Altus, Grace T., 45, 46

Analysis of covariance, 33, 36-37, 146

Anastasi, Ann, 3

Anderson, A. L., 57

Angular gyrus, 8, 9-10

Aphasia: definition, 5-6; theories, 6; test results, 60-64

Asymmetry of talent, 3, 130

Auditory abilities, 141-142

Auditory input, 51-52

Austin, G. A., 139

Bauer, R. W., 57

Becka, D. M., 57

Belmont, Lillian, 12, 13

Bender, Lauretta, 10

Bender Gestalt Test, 10-11, 12

Benton, A. L., 5, 30, 65, 133

BIMD computer programs, 33

Birch, H. G., 11, 12, 13, 29, 65-66, 133

Booker, H. L., 72

Boring, E. G., 4

Boyer, Ann, 140

Brain damage. *See* cerebral dysfunction

Brain, W. R., 5

Broadbent, W. H., 6

Bruce, P., 45

Bruner, J. S., 139

Burks, H. F., 45

Carrigan, Patricia, 10

Carter, R. P., 84

Case history: method, 30; procedure, 31-32; results, 72-84; interpretation, 146

Cattell, R. B., 92

Cerebral dominance, 4n, 4-5; incomplete, 8-9, 133

Cerebral dysfunction: and human abilities, 4-5; angular gyrus, 8, 9-10; lateralized, 28-29, 57-58, 89-90; nonlateralized, 58-59; estimate of probability, 35, 85-91, 146; related to reading disability, 133-134, 148

Cherry, C., 139

Coan, R. W., 99

Cohn, R., 55

Computer programs, BIMD, 33

Costa, L. D., 57

Critchley, 4, 6, 8, 9, 13, 14, 17

Cruz, Caridad, 15, 31, 72

de Hirsch, Katrina, 10-11, 29, 66

Developmental history, 73-82

Directional confusion, 9-10, 29, 64-65, 133

Discriminant analysis: method, 34, 100-101, 106; results, 106-110; interpretation, 111, 147

Doehring, D. G., 57, 129, 143

Donaldson, R. W., 140

Drew, A. L., 8, 12, 15, 25, 30, 34, 70

Dunn, L. M., 24

Dyslexia: developmental, 1, 13; in aphasic patients, 6-7

Eden, M., 140

Factor analysis: and assessment of abilities, 3; method, 33, 92-93; results, 93-99; interpretation, 99, 147

Family history, 30, 80-82

Farrant, R. H., 92

Ferguson, G. A., 143

Fuller, Ann, 15

Gagné, R. M., 143

Gaito, J., 10

Galanter, E., 139

Garton, Jeanette, 12, 45, 46, 48

Generalized stepwise regression. *See* Multiple stepwise regression

Gerstmann's syndrome, 9-10, 64-65

Geschwind, N., 6-7

Gestalt disturbance, 10-11, 66, 133